NOW
OR
NEVER

D. S. HALACY, JR.

NOW OR NEVER

the fight against pollution

FOUR WINDS PRESS/NEW YORK

By the same author

CENTURY TWENTY-ONE: YOUR LIFE IN THE YEAR 2001
  & BEYOND
COLONIZATION OF THE MOON
COMING AGE OF SOLAR ENERGY
COMPUTERS: THE MACHINES WE THINK WITH
ENERGY AND ENGINES
HABITAT: MAN'S UNIVERSE AND ECOLOGY
MAN ALIVE
ROBOTS ARE HERE
ROCKET RESCUE
SKY ON FIRE
SURFER
WATER CRISIS: A BACKGROUND STUDY ANALYZING WAYS &
  MEANS OF SUPPLYING WATER FOR A GROWING WORLD
CHARLES BABBAGE: FATHER OF THE COMPUTER

This book is printed on 100% recycled paper.

Published by Four Winds Press
A Division of Scholastic Magazines, Inc., New York, N.Y.
Copyright © 1971 D. S. Halacy, Jr.
All rights reserved.
Printed in the United States of America
Library of Congress Catalogue Card Number: 71-161018

CONTENTS

NOW
OR
NEVER

This is the natural beauty of America that is becoming harder and harder to find.

—SIERRA CLUB

1

POLLUTION: CHALLENGE OF
THE SEVENTIES

And the Lord God took the man, and put him
into the Garden of Eden to dress it and to keep it.

Genesis 2:15

In the 1970's we have attained the dubious distinction of
being the most affluent people of all time. We earn more and
spend more than ever before in history. Science and technology flourish, giving us power and other material blessings
on a scale which once would not have seemed possible. We
are beginning to triumph over disease and even poverty;
education is more widespread than in the past. Transportation, with some notable exceptions, is fast, efficient, and
economical. Communication is instantaneously achieved on
a worldwide basis. In short, the level of civilization has
reached an all-time high. Unfortunately, these material blessings have also given our society another distinction—this
one clearly no credit to mankind. For the 1970's promise to
be the *dirtiest* years in history too. Man has not "dressed and
kept" his Garden of Eden, and that is our problem today.

Of all the crises facing us—and there are many—it is

pollution that we hear about most. We also *see* it, *smell* it, *taste* it, *eat* it, *drink* it, and *stumble* through it. We literally live in and breathe filth, and, not surprisingly, it is beginning to threaten our health, our happiness, and our very civilization. The growing outcries against pollution are not exaggerated alarms. In 1970 an estimated $1 billion damage was caused in the United States to agricultural crops alone. The total bill for pollution of various kinds is probably more than $14 billion annually. Americans—and others around the world, for pollution plays no favorites—breathe air containing toxic poisons and harmful chemicals that not only rot rubber and leather, dissolve nylon stockings, and erode stone, but *kill* plants, animals, and men. Respiratory diseases that for years have taken a heavy toll in smoggy London are now increasing in the United States. Some of us drink water the Public Health Service declares unfit for consumption, water fouled by sewage from communities lucky enough to be upstream from the source of supply. Our food contains deadly poisons as does food everywhere on the globe. Such substances as DDT and lead are found even in the most remote polar regions.

It is historical fact that man is wasteful, and now his wastes are beginning to bury him. He walks through once-sunny places with his head swathed in dirty brown smoke that stings the eyes and irritates the throat and lungs. He tries to swim in a once-clean river, lake, or ocean. And he fights his way through mountains of trash and garbage that are beginning to overwhelm him. Every year each of us discards a *ton* of solid waste; a family of four produces 8,000 pounds of such refuse, in addition to the tons of liquid waste flushed down the clogged sewers of the nation, and to the tons of pollutants introduced into the air.

There is visual pollution across our blighted land, visible not only to airplane passengers six miles up, but also to

The loss of our precious recreational facilities is just one of the prices we pay for pollution. This forbidden beach is located on Lake Michigan.
—ENVIRONMENTAL PROTECTION AGENCY

astronauts thousands of miles out in space. Airline pilots often characterize Los Angeles as a "tobacco stain on the ground"; frequently they must carry extra fuel for proceeding to an alternate airport because of low visibility caused by the smog. The "tobacco stain" is more than a nuisance. A former head of the National Cancer Institute has described it as "a sea of carcinogens," or cancer-inducing agents. In that sea, more than fifty pollutants have been identified, including arsenic, asphalt, benzol, carbon black, chromium, creosote, mustard gas, paraffin, and tar.

Not long ago the smog of Los Angeles was treated by comedians as a great joke, but lately there has been a taper-

Problem: find the hidden city. Smog is no longer a laughing matter in places like this. —NATIONAL OCEANIC AND ATMOSPHERIC ADMINISTRATION

The "poison" that killed these fish was sugar beet wastes dumped into the stream they once inhabited. —U. S. DEPARTMENT OF AGRICULTURE

ing off of such humor. Smog is no longer native only to California. A Laramie, Wyoming resident describing a local cement plant, says it "spews gases, soot, and dust particles over much of the area. Houses and cars, livestock and pets have a dull slate gray appearance due to the clouds of wastes settling on them."

In many locations school children are brought indoors when health officials decide that pollution has reached dangerously high levels. And hospitals provide "clean rooms" for respiratory disease patients. General Motors researchers studying motor vehicle pollution must pass the outside air through a five-stage filter before it is pure enough to meet test standards.

In New York's Trinity Church cemetery gravestones have been treated to prevent corrosion by sulfur dioxide in the air. Ironically, there are more headstones to treat too. Air pollution is a major factor in causing emphysema, which kills nearly 50,000 Americans a year. (In the days of Sir William Osler, a noted British physician, emphysema was attributed to "airway resistance" and classed as an occupational disease of trombone players!) Air pollution and smoking are the chief causes of chronic bronchitis, which is the *leading* cause of death in England for men over forty-five and the fourth highest for the population as a whole. Lung cancer occurs twice as often in air-polluted cities as in rural areas. Pollution also contributes to the common cold, pneumonia, and bronchial asthma.

At the 1962 meeting of the National Conference on Air Pollution, Surgeon General Luther L. Terry stated that approximately ninety percent of our urban population lived in localities with air-pollution problems. Yet we were spending only about ten cents per person to clean up the air—a problem which costs each of us about $65 every year in money spent on cleaning bills, automobile tires, agricultural

waste, and so on. A later estimate for health damage caused
by pollution in the air was $2 billion for the year 1963. In
1966, Surgeon General William H. Stewart stated bluntly:
"The threat to health, in my opinion, constitutes the primary
impulse for the control of air pollution in the United States."

Japan knows the tragedy of pollution as well as we do.
Smog enshrouds Tokyo and other cities. There is a disease
called Minimata Bay sickness, caused by industrial mercury
in the water and, hence, in the seafood the Japanese eat.
There is also "Yokohama asthma," attributed to industrial
smog. A similar disease has been noted in New Orleans,
incidentally.

One type of European moth has evolved a new species,
know as *carbonaria*, in less than a hundred years! Its darker
coloration blends protectively with smog-blackened vegetation. Here is a phenomenon that supports Darwin's theory
of "natural selection" to preserve life. All life is not so
adaptable, of course. Smog can cut average grape yields by
as much as sixty percent; Zinfandel grapes produce 6.9
pounds of fruit per vine in smog and 17.8 pounds in clean air.

What Quality of Life?

Pollution is a dirty word. It is a complex word too. Once we
thought of pollution as simply meaning smog—the choking,
stinging, dirty clouds of irritants that hug the cities. But air
pollution, while it is still the most dangerous and therefore
the most talked about, is only one type of contamination
among several which attack the most basic life functions.

We have made septic tanks of many lakes, rivers, and
estuaries. We are polluting the oceans too. Some bodies of
water are so filthy that fish die. Senator Jennings Randolph,
Chairman of the Committee on Public Works, charges that

of thirty-three rivers in our country that once had salmon runs, only six now provide a home for this valuable fish. Europe's Rhine, which once teemed with salmon, can no longer support them. The Cuyahoga River in the United States recently burst into flames, so contaminated is it with chemicals!

Man has created not only great cities but disgusting slums. He has dug a wealth of mineral resources, and left ugly gashes across the once-lovely landscape. He has built roadways that have desecrated what beauty there was left in the cities and blighted rural areas with miles of concrete and countless ugly billboards.

In his struggle to produce more and more food to feed the increasing population, man has polluted farms, fields, water, and air with thousands of pesticide poisons. A less obvious, but more insidious pollution is caused by atomic power plants, whose radioactive gases and solid wastes represent a potential danger to all living things.

In addition to all these pollutions, there has lately been added another—noise pollution—which comes from our machines and vehicles, the noise of construction, production and destruction. The noise of transportation, of amplified music and non-music, attacks our eardrums, our minds, and our bodies in ways now beginning to alarm doctors and scientists.

It is often easy to block out the realities of pollution. There are some days and some places that are nice and clear, and after all, isn't it part of progress? But pollution is costing us billions of dollars each year—some estimates show that a family living in New York City loses about $850 annually— and it is a serious threat to health. Some respected scientists even fear that pollution is changing the weather and may be affecting long-range climate disastrously. But the gravest threat is the danger pollution presents to the quality of life.

Dr. Rene Dubos, noted bacteriologist and author of *So*

Human An Animal, and one of those most concerned with man's dirtying of the environment, has pointed out a strange and terrible occurrence in pollution experiments with animals. A bird placed suddenly in an environment of heavily polluted air falls over dead in a few minutes. A bird whose environment is *slowly poisoned* does not die but adapts to the poison. But what sort of life is this? What agonies does the animal undergo in order to continue its "life" in a polluted environment? And what price are we paying? Dr. Dubos comments:

> . . . each one of us is constantly being shaped by his total environment as much as by his genetic endowment . . .
>
> The greatest crime committed in American cities may not be murder, rape, or robbery, but rather the wholesale and constant exposure of children to noise, ugliness and garbage in the street, thereby conditioning them to accept public squalor as the normal state of affairs and diminishing their future enjoyment of life.

Sometimes pollution just seems to occur naturally. But pollution is an *act,* something done by polluters. None of us is blameless, for even in the simple and necessary process of breathing we can pollute the air. And few of us just sit around breathing. Certain kinds of pollution are inevitable; even the animals contribute these. But man, with his technology of power production, industry, transportation, and a host of other more-or-less necessary activities, far outdoes nature as a polluter. As we wallow in the poisons and irritants of our environment it is ironic to complain, because we ourselves have put most of them there.

Today, as every day, we used the plumbing at home or elsewhere. We drove a car, or used some kind of powered transportation. We consumed fuel—coal, gas, or oil. We bought a product in a bottle, can, box, sack, or other package.

Even dead, we pollute the environment unless sealed in a container that will never expose us to soil, water, or air.

Most of us do not work in mines that pour out tons of sulfur dioxide and other pollutants. Relatively few of us operate nuclear power plants that leak radioactivity and thermally pollute a water supply. We may not even have flown in a plane that spews pollutants into skies no longer clear and blue. But we used the products of the mine. We turned on a light or a TV set. We sent a letter that traveled in a kerosene-burning plane or a diesel locomotive.

Dr. Morris Neuberger, writing in the *Bulletin of the American Meteorological Society,* visualized the frightening prospects:

Looking into my smoggy crystal ball I see alternately two visions of the future—let us say the year 2064—one pessimistic and disheartening, the other optimistic, hopeful, and probably unreal.

The pessimistic view is that in the course of the next century, as the population grows, as the power demands per capita increase both in the already industrialized nations and in the developing countries where there is so much need for it, the amount of waste poured into the atmosphere by these activities will far exceed the atmosphere's capacity to diffuse and to remove the waste, and the atmosphere will grow progressively more polluted until, a century from now, the air is too toxic to permit human life. All of civilization will pass away, not from a sudden cataclysm, but from gradual suffocation by its own effluents.

Such a prospect is not pleasant to face, so we shall not face it and do something about it, but instead will let it creep up on us. Only after it has progressed to the point where it will be extremely difficult and expensive to take any steps to combat it will the public be aroused to demand that something be done. And even then people will be unwilling to have any of their own activities curtailed or to have their own taxes increased to pay for the effort to prevent the disaster.

Mankind will sink into its smoggy doom through inertia and irresponsibility. . . .

The more pleasant prospect of my other vision . . . is based on the unlikely premise that humans will at some time in the near future take stock of their relationship to the natural resources on which the very existence of human life and civilization is based. . . .

We cannot forever sweep the mess under the rug. Suddenly our crimes over the years have caught up with us, and we are looking in the mirror of environment and seeing the horrible accumulated results.

In his 1969 Smithsonian Lecture, Rene Dubos made this comment:

All archaic peoples, all ancient classical cultures, have practiced some form of nature religion. Even in our times a large number of isolated, primitive tribes in Australia, in Africa, and in South America still experience a feeling of holiness for the land in which they live. In contrast, respect for the earth and for nature has almost completely disappeared from industrialized people in most of the countries that have accepted the ways of western civilization.

We must renew our lost respect for the earth and for nature. There are various reasons for this crisis of environment; all have a bearing on the problem, and all must be considered in shaping solutions.

"Popullution"

When Columbus reached North America some five centuries ago the continent supported perhaps one million human beings. Man was well in tune with nature in those days because there was so much nature and so few men. In *all* the world there were only about 440 million inhabitants. With some notable exceptions, the natural clean-up mechanisms of water, wind, air, and natural decomposition functioned well enough to tidy up man's mess.

Today's problems of pollution are tied to exploding population; in fact the term "popullution" is sometimes used to describe the situation. More people produce more wastes. But the problem is even worse than mounting numbers, for where earlier man produced a certain amount of waste per capita, today he produces many times that as a by-product of his higher standard of living. Ours has been called the "affluent society," and rightly so. But just as rightly it is known as an "effluent society."

Man produces no more body wastes individually than he ever did. But all the material goods we use today, coupled with our "throw-away" technology, results in far more waste per capita. Today we pitch into the trash barrel containers of metal, glass, or plastic that would have once been considered valuable. Although few people really do trade in their automobiles as soon as the ashtrays fill up, not many of us make the full use of vehicles that our grandfathers did. There is a danger in this practice far beyond pollution, in that we are wasting our limited natural resources. Part of the answer to pollution may be a more tight-fisted, intelligent use of these resources, and the realization that when they are gone there are no more. And many of these precious resources are already in short supply.

It is ecologically stylish to refer to a so-called "cowboy economy" as one which destroys natural resources because there is such an abundance of them. Actually the cowboys in American history might be horrified at today's wasteful "throw-away" philosophy. With little material at hand, the cowboy was a master at recycling. Using barbed wire and bits of wood, he fashioned practical and long-lived gates

Mines can take more than minerals from the earth. This desecration was caused by strip mining. —U. S. DEPARTMENT OF AGRICULTURE

Solid wastes of various kinds combine to produce blighted neighborhoods. At least once cars are abandoned they no longer cause air pollution. —ENVIRONMENTAL PROTECTION AGENCY

This kind of water pollution, unsightly as it seems, is easier to clean up than some less visible pollutants in our waterways. Understandably, residents of Red Boiling Springs, Tennessee, formed a Development Association to clean up such messes.

—U. S. DEPARTMENT OF AGRICULTURE

Air travel has left its mark all across the country, including our nation's capital. This plane is landing at National Airport near Washington, D. C.

—ENVIRONMENTAL PROTECTION AGENCY

to keep his cattle on the range. When clothes or blankets or saddles wore out he patched them or used them for some other purpose. Cowhide could serve as a cabin door; bones were burned and used as fertilizer. An abandoned wagon provided wheels for another vehicle and wood for a fire or perhaps even a shed. Bits of metal were eagerly sought and used as hinges, braces, axles, and for other needs. The canvas top of a prairie schooner might make a tent, or even clothes. When automobiles began to invade ranches, junked Model T's provided tires for children's swings, or to be burned to ward off the cold or the bees. Sheet metal patched holes in buildings, and celluloid side curtains were tacked over open windows. A salvaged engine might power a winch or a hoist rigged up in the barn, and its metal shafts served as stakes for the game of horseshoes, just as the horseshoes themselves were used to good purpose after Dobbin had finished with them.

Contrast this salvaging of parts with our habit of throwing away just about everything. For a number of reasons many people find it cheaper to drive an old car out somewhere and simply abandon it. Instead of paying the "fixit" man to repair a toaster or radio, we buy a new one and throw out the old, even though ninety-five percent of its parts may still be functioning. Television sets are designed with throw-away parts; it is cheaper to install new ones than to try to repair a malfunctioning component. Who is to blame for this economic creation of trash piles—the manufacturer who designs such equipment, or the buyer who pays him? Is *anyone* to blame, or are we all?

Check the number of trash barrels your family has, and how often you fill them with discarded paper, cans, bottles, and other "trash." Many large newspapers weigh several pounds; valuable newsprint consumes our limited resources of wood and could be reused in making more paper.

Technological Man

While increased consumption of material goods produces more waste, it is in the generation and consumption of power that man offends most. The problems of pollution are largely problems of combustion, the burning of fuel to produce power for a variety of uses.

Smoke was here on earth before man came along to complain about it. Greek legends credit Prometheus with bringing fire down from heaven, and early in his development man learned how to use it for his own benefit. Fire kept him warm, cooked his food and protected him from wild beasts.

Over the years man began to use fire in his various industries. Metals were smelted with fire; glass could be made with it. Then came the heat engine. Where once wind and water—clean, "natural" energy sources—had been converted into useful power, steam engines and internal-combustion engines began to snort and pop in the industrialized countries. Today there are almost a hundred million vehicles in the United States. The horse has given way to the automobile; horseback riding has become recreation rather than transportation for most of the world. The airplane has joined surface vehicles and ships as a consumer of fuel.

Next time you take a trip, think for a moment how it would be to travel that distance on horseback or in a buggy. The kind of world to which we are accustomed depends on diesel or gasoline engines, on jets or gas turbines. And these in turn depend on the combustion of fuel—the mixture of that fuel with oxygen from the air to produce power as well as such byproducts as smoke, fumes and particles. This is the price of progress, the inevitable pollution of our environment by the engines we have built to serve us. Few human slaves remain in the world, to the credit of enlightened mankind. But those of us in the developed countries call on the services of mechanical slaves by the hundreds in our homes, our offices, our schools, recreational facilities, factories, and transportation.

Buckminster Fuller, inventor and engineer, has estimated that in 1940 Americans were each using power equivalent to that of 153 human slaves. In 1970 he upped this figure to 500 slaves! Thus the per capita consumption of power has more than tripled in just thirty years. In that same period population in the United States has also increased, from 133 million to 206 million. We are now using about thirteen tons of materials per person each year. We use 350 *billion* gallons of water a day. One writer speculates that ten billion "natural" men could not put the strain on our country that 206 million technologically-oriented ones do.

In our demand for ever-increasing power we consequently create a demand for energy in the form of various fuels. Wood long ago lost the capability of providing sufficient power even for steam engines. Today the cost of wood is so high that it is expensive to burn a fire in the fireplace except as a luxury. Instead we gouge the earth for coal and pierce it for gas and oil; strange spindle-legged rigs probe for oil miles off our shores. All too often something goes wrong and millions of gallons of fuel are spilled in an accidental pollution that has only totally negative effects.

We're All in This Together

Is there a solution, short of wearing a gas mask when traveling, and spending most of our days in a lead-lined room subsisting on distilled water and "organic" foods? Must we journey to the moon and build a new environment there, carefully avoiding the mistakes we have made on the earth?

If man is to blame for most of the pollution that threatens him, it should be obvious that man can also lessen that amount. There are hopeful signs—some of them in the sky—that he will do this.

London, historically a serious offender in the crime of pollution, a city where thousands have died from its effects, now wears a new and cleaner face. Why? Because a majority of its citizens agreed at last to do something about pollution that disfigured the city. Today the air—and the water—is clearer and cleaner there than in many cities that don't even realize they have a pollution problem. Londoners are seeing more birds, in more varieties, than they have for decades. They are admiring famous and historic landmarks, buildings washed clean of the grime that for centuries hid their original and intended beauty. More importantly, fewer Englishmen are doomed to die of bronchitis and other pollution-induced diseases.

Less dramatically but just as encouragingly, improvement has been made in some of our cities, among them Pittsburgh and Los Angeles. Most significant is the fact that many of us are demanding that action be taken against pollution. Nationwide demonstrations such as "Earth Day," as well as pollution clinics and other activities, are involving millions in the fight. Legislators and administrators are belatedly taking heed. So are large-scale polluters—mines and mills, the auto industry, aircraft builders and operators. Our leaders in Washington have made pollution a top priority problem; they are expending huge sums of money and enlisting the help of thousands of people in efforts to clean up our environment.

All polluters are not callously indifferent to the mess they are making and to the dangers they are creating to life. Some have made sincere, continuing, and very expensive efforts to clean up the wastes they are dumping into the environment. A complex technology has been developed in many factories for trapping pollutants before they enter the atmosphere. For decades factories have had scrubbers and baggers and such sophisticated anti-pollution devices as electrostatic precipitators. Although some environmentalists seem to believe otherwise, engines have also been designed to minimize exhaust. Had they not, pollution would be thick enough to cut with a knife, and Los Angeles' notorious smog would be clean air by comparison.

There are exceptions, of course. Some selfish industries have made it a practice to clean up only as much as they are required to. For years some have used the "empty stomach" threat to ward off any improvements in their dirty operations. "Which do you want, blue sky or a job?" is the argument. "Try to make us clean up and we'll move!" is another threat. And in many cases these tactics work.

Just as shortsighted as some polluters are environmentalists who see the solution in "lynching a few smelter operators" as an example to all. Panic and hysteria may be useful in calling attention to pollution problems, but they will not solve those problems. We must begin by being aware of the causes of pollution, and most of them stem from our necessary and everyday activities. It has been said that there are some very simple solutions to pollution: We must stop using our automobiles, trains, buses, ships, and airplanes. Stop using electrical power and gas heat. Stop using the bathroom and stop filling the trash cans. Such solutions are simple to the point of being idiotic, of course. We might as well ask also that we stop breathing and carrying out other bodily functions.

Like any worthwhile goal, there is a huge price tag on success. It may cost Americans some $100 billion in the next few years to clean up the air and water and properly dispose of solid wastes. But what is this sum compared with the total expenditures of our country? Over a ten-year period it will be less than three percent of our budget, only a fraction of our military expenditures. Best of all, we will most likely find that cleaning up will eventually *pay* us in countless ways instead of costing. We all stand to benefit from a cleaner world.

Life must go on, and living causes pollution. The solution lies in the wisest compromise we can make, the happiest bargain we can strike. We shall never achieve the dream environment of "preservationists" if we are to use that environment. After all, is there beauty in something no one enjoys or uses? The trick is to use without *abusing* too much. If life is to go on, pollution is inevitable. But some of it *must* be eliminated or reduced if life as we would like it to be is to prevail.

2

POLLUTION: AN AGE-OLD PROBLEM

*Farmers around Butte, Montana, have
organized to make a fight against the owners
of the ore smelters in that vicinity, which,
it is claimed, have ruined the agricultural industry
of that section. The statement is made by the
farmers that no less than five tons of sulphuric
acid and half that amount of arsenic are
discharged into the air daily, and that the crops
for a great many miles around are affected.*

Scientific American, March, 1903

Although the present widespread public clamor against pollution is relatively new, the problem itself is older than man. Take water pollution, for instance. The oceans are a classic example of water so contaminated that it is unsuited to most of man's domestic and industrial uses. But it was not man but nature which did most of that polluting. The salt and other pollutants in the seas, representing a sizable three percent of the total, were scoured from the land as rainwaters made their way back to the ocean. Here is pollution amounting to one part in thirty-three; we are alarmed in some cases when man-made pollution amounts to one part in a *million!*

The ocean, itself polluted, is a polluter too. It contaminates the air with salt that does incalculable damage. If you live near the ocean you may be familiar with the rusting and pitting of car parts caused by salt air.

Not just the oceans but rivers too were polluted long before man began dumping sewage and industrial wastes into them. Again erosion is the culprit, as water gouges out rocks, dirt, and other foreign matter on its downhill journey to the sea. Animal wastes pollute water, as do droppings from plants and trees. There is a river in Mississippi that runs black with tannic acid from leaves that fall into it. Creatures luckless enough to blunder into the river can die from the poisoned water.

Captain John Smith reported that great numbers of dead fish floated all around his boat on the Potomac River, back in 1608! This, of course, was long before the advent of sawmills, chemical plants, or pesticides and must be attributed to nature. Of course the decaying matter of the dead fish themselves add to the pollution problem.

All nature's creatures are not the neat nonpolluters that one might think. Some animals live in one place until they have so fouled it that it is uninhabitable; then they move on to a spot as yet unspoiled. Fortunately only a few humans in modern times behave in this manner, although the littering of beautiful country picnic spots occurs far too often.

Nature also pollutes the air—about 2,000 times as much as man does. According to Dr. Robert D. Englert, executive director of one of Stanford Research Institute's laboratories, manmade pollutants amount to about 500 million tons a year. Yet total air pollution amounts to one *trillion* tons!

It is difficult to define a "pure" environment, since perhaps only a total vacuum would qualify in all regards, but a vacuum is not particularly useful for living things. At one time the earth had no atmosphere and had to create its own. Living organisms helped make that atmosphere, and the air we breathe is the result of interaction between atmosphere and the forms of life that depend on it for survival.

The natural atmosphere consists of oxygen, nitrogen, some carbon dioxide, water vapor, and a few gases; other substances in the air may be classed as pollutants. Here again nature has contributed heavily. Volcanoes hurl gases more than 70,000 feet into the air, and with the gases are smoke and debris. A single volcano may put a hundred billion cubic yards of fine particles into the atmosphere, particles that remain there for years. In the vicinity of the volcano this represents a direct hazard to life, as we know from the eruption of Vesuvius, which buried the city of Pompeii in 79 A.D., or Krakatoa, which erupted in 1883. Even far away we may be affected, since the pollutants decrease the inflow of solar energy and thus cool the earth; this is what happened after Krakatoa. Debris in the air from volcanoes is also responsible for more pleasant phenomena, including the beautifully colored sunrises and sunsets we enjoy. So some pollution can be a mixed blessing.

Besides water erosion there is wind erosion, and dust storms are common in many places. In the 1930's wind turned the American Southwest into a desolate area aptly called the Dust Bowl. While man contributed to that catastrophe by unwisely plowing the land, nature furnished the dust and wind that polluted the skies as far away as New York City.

Most of us know that in the process of photosynthesis, on which practically all life depends, plants take up carbon

Soil erosion and debris contribute to unsightly pollution in Fairfax, Virginia. Strangely enough, some people still consider our waterways mere dumping grounds. —U. S. DEPARTMENT OF AGRICULTURE

Nature too is a polluter. This active volcano is Santiaguito in Guatemala and was photographed some years ago.

—U. S. DEPARTMENT OF AGRICULTURE

What a forest fire started, erosion continues, resulting in lost forest and grasslands, as well as pollution of streams below.
—U. S. DEPARTMENT OF AGRICULTURE

Lightning causes many fires, but man helps create havoc in our forests far too often. Fortunately this fire on Wolf Creek in Oregon was confined to about 100 acres.
—U. S. DEPARTMENT OF AGRICULTURE

dioxide from the air and return oxygen in exchange. Most of us are not aware, however, of other emanations from plants and trees, including those called "terpenes." Such huge quantities of these substances are given off that they constitute an appreciable portion of the pollutants in the atmosphere. Some meteorologists believe that terpenes may affect precipitation by acting as condensation nuclei for raindrops on snowflakes.

Plants also put pollen into the air, and pollen, while it is important in plant reproduction, produces physical discomfort and even illness in some humans and animals allergic to it. Indeed, pollen is a major cause of sickness.

Forest fires, most of them started by lightning, burn off about six million acres of forests in the United States each decade. Here is a tremendous amount of natural pollution. Dust particles blown into the air by wind may remain there for weeks before they are washed out by rain or snow. Animals aid the wind in stirring up dust, and nature also spreads disease in animals and insects, bacteria and viruses.

The atmosphere is also being polluted by cosmic dust from outer space. Each year some 1,000 tons of cosmic micrometeorites shower the earth. Compared with other pollution sources, a thousand tons is not significant, but it is an unusual source of pollution.

Man: The Master Polluter

But while nature must shoulder the blame for much pollution of the environment, as well as for the loss of countless millions of human lives, nature also has the power to heal its ravages. In time a burned-out forest grows back; an island wiped clean of all living things flourishes with life again after several decades. A fouled river has its water purified by passage through the sea, distillation, and condensation as rain. The sea of air is so vast that winds and time can dilute poisons so that they are tolerable.

It was man and his scientific "revolutions" that upset nature's healing balance. These revolutions are generally considered three in number.

First came the toolmaking revolution; the spears and other weapons it produced enabled man to defend himself against animals and also to kill more animals for food. The human population grew.

Revolution number two was the agricultural revolution, a giant step which made it possible for an acre of land planted with crops to support ten times as many people as an acre providing only fruits, berries, and game.

The third revolution came when the agricultural revolution led in turn to a science and technology explosion. This was the industrial revolution, a mixed blessing which provides our material goods but which also creates pollution problems.

Man upset the applecart of ecology when he began to gather in large numbers. He began to build cities and to burn fuel which choked the air with smoke. With thousands of people clustered together in a small area, nature could not get rid of body wastes and other pollutants safely and quickly enough. Ironically, man was not aware for a long time that there even *was* a problem. After all, he thought, waste was natural; nature would take care of it.

To learn how old our pollution problems really are we have only to read about ancient ways of life. More than 4,000 years ago, the great Babylonian king Hammurabi wrote: "When Anu and Enlil gave me the lands of Sumer and Akkad to rule, and they entrusted this sceptre to me, I dug the canal *Hammurabinukjush-nishi*, which bringeth copious water to the land of Sumer and Akkad. Its banks on both sides I turned into cultivated ground; I heaped up piles of grain, I provided unfailing water for the lands."

But what brought the mighty Babylon down? According to scientist Paul B. Sears, it was agricultural pollution of its water: "Babylon disintegrated because for centuries the operation of agriculture had been increasingly burdened by heavy loads of silt in the life-giving canals."

Later, greater civilizations also fought losing battles with pollution. Greece fell to Rome, and the Romans fell to a variety of pollutions, among them lead poisoning. Despite the repeated warnings of the engineer Vitruvius and the physician Galen against the use of toxic lead in the plumbing, Rome continued the practice because the lead was non-corrosive and long lasting. There is controversy over how major a factor lead poisoning really was, but of other pollution there is little question. Historian Will Durant has this to say in *The Story of Civilization:*

> Farmers complained that high taxes consumed their precarious profits and left them too little to keep the drainers and irrigation canals in repair; the canals filled up, the marshes spread, and malaria weakened the population of Campagna and Rome.

> In central and southern Italy deforestation, erosion, and the neglect of irrigation canals by a diminishing peasantry and a disordered government had left Italy poorer than before.

> Epidemics of major proportions decimated the population under Aurelius, Gallienus, and Constantine. In the plague of 260–65 almost every family in the Empire was attacked; in Rome, we are told, there were 5,000 deaths every day for many weeks. The mosquitoes of the Campagna were winning their war against the human invaders of the pontine marshes and malaria was sapping the strength of rich and poor in Latrium and Tuscany.

The "Yearbook of Agriculture," published by the U. S. Department of Agriculture in 1955, comments in this way on Rome's fall:

> . . . The constant warfare and political disturbances broke down social concerns over water supplies, among other important public services. As ignorance and poverty increased, sanitary precautions came to mean less and less, and in time cleanliness was frowned upon as evidence of wicked thoughts and self-indulgence. Bathing, formerly widely practiced for its therapeutic values, was abandoned. The citizens no longer took pride in clean homes and streets, which became filthier and filthier. Worst of all, the water, obtained mostly from wells, eventually became so fouled as to be unfit for use.

Ironically, Rome's waterworks were so remarkably advanced that they make some systems today appear crude by comparison. Vitruvius and others pioneered the idea of water quality. Drinking water for kings was boiled and stored in silver flasks. Filters were made from a variety of materials, from wool to tufa blocks. Vitruvius tested water for contaminants. There were three supply systems. One furnished private homes through metered pipes which permitted the water commissioners to present accurate bills to the owners. Another system supplied the public baths, with a charge again made against the users. There was a third supply system for the magnificent pools and fountains.

Actually, the situation in our country is a far cry from the pollution that prevailed in Europe after the fall of Rome. Instead of inside plumbing, the outside privy prevailed and was often adjacent to the well that provided water for domestic use! As towns and cities grew, the inevitable pollution of water by sewage occurred with increasing frequency. London was a prime example. Only after the horrible Black Death, in the fourteenth century, and widespread outbreaks of cholera, plus the linking of these diseases to water-borne germs and solid wastes, did men begin to provide relatively pure water and to guard against its pollution.

London grew with industrialization, and wells could no longer provide sufficient water. In 1581 the London Bridge Waterworks began to supply municipal water, pumping four million gallons to residents daily. And the new "water closets," which had now replaced the dangerous outdoor toilets, carried wastes to sewer systems. Interestingly, the water company pumped its supply out of the Thames River —and the sewer emptied back into the Thames.

Using the same water source as both supply and sewer is distasteful, but what was the alternative? Londoners had learned that they could not continue to maintain privies and wells side by side and hope to escape from terrible diseases. Didn't the water of the Thames move along and sweep the waste out to sea, where it would be no problem? As long as domestic water was taken upstream of the sewer pipes, all would be well—except, of course, for anyone downstream. Our water problems today have a heritage going back four centuries and more.

While London's water pollution was responsible for many deaths, it is for air pollution that the city was most notorious. London was the breeding ground of industrialization, whose new sources of man-made pollution added their outpouring of smoke to the atmosphere. The problem of air pollution began long before James Watt perfected his wheezing and clanking steam engine, however.

Although wood smoke is often a nuisance, in general it can be tolerated. But centuries ago, as man burned more and more wood and supplies dwindled, peat, and then coal, were used as substitutes. A new industry was born, and a new pollutant added to already smoky, foggy London.

Although coal had been burned for some time in Asia,

the Church of England loudly protested its use. If heathens in China wanted to burn this "unnatural" fuel, that was their concern, but the Church was opposed to Englishmen dabbling with "hellfire and brimstone." Indeed, coal *was* a different fuel from the "natural" wood, although it began as vegetation millions of years ago. But coal, unlike wood, contains sulfur, and sulfur dioxide is one of the worst pollutants. In spite of the Church and the smoke and fumes, however, the "unnatural" fuel was sold in great quantities to homeowners and to industry.

The population of London continued to increase, and its people and industries dumped even greater quantities of coal smoke and other pollutants into the skies. Then in December of 1873 the weather conspired with pollution to produce a thick, choking cloud for days. Some 1,150 people died during this time from causes associated with air pollution. Similar winter disasters occurred in London in 1880, 1882, 1891 and 1892.

London was not alone. Glasgow, Scotland, having neither the size nor the industrial might of London, nevertheless suffered a similar tragedy in the fall of 1909. More than 1,000 deaths were blamed on the combination of smoke and fog. In making a report of the catastrophe Dr. Harold Antoine Des Voeux was first to use the word "smog," a contraction formed by joining smoke and fog.

There's A Law Against Pollution

Today we applaud "tough" anti-pollution laws, as we begin to crack down on those who dirty up the environment. But there is a history of concern over pollution, dating back seven hundred years and more.

In 1273 King Edward I promoted passage of a law out-

lawing the use of coal. But such a ban was almost like trying
to stop people from breathing. The smoke grew steadily
worse and in 1306 the British Parliament set up a commission to combat the smoke in London. Part of the proclama-
tion forbad the use of coal in furnaces, and shortly after the
law was passed a coal merchant was hanged for violating it.
But pollution went on unabated in spite of this harsh warning. Men had to have heat for their homes, for industrial
furnaces and for other uses, and coal provided that heat
So the problem continued and then worsened as there were
more people, more industry, and more coal burned.

In the late 1300's, King Richard III put a high tax on
coal (the idea of taxing polluters is nothing new!), and later
Henry V formed a smoke commission for London. Charles
II, in 1661 and with the smoke more choking than ever,
turned to science for the answer. He commissioned John
Evelyn to conduct a survey of the problem, and Evelyn
produced what was probably the first air pollution report,
entitled *Fumifugium*, which is Latin for "The Dispelling of
Smoke." Evelyn linked the "smokes" of London to many
diseases and disorders: " . . . Her Inhabitants breathe nothing but an impure and thick Mist, accompanied with a
fuliginous and filthy vapour, which renders them obnoxious
to a thousand inconveniences, corrupting the Lungs, and
disordering the entire habit of their Bodies; so that Catarrhs,
Phthsicks, Coughs, and Consumptions, rage more in this
one City, than in the whole Earth besides."

Fumifugium was duly filed away, and the city continued
its smoky ways. Writer Francois Chateaubriand described a
visit to London in 1822: "Soon I saw before me the black
skullcap which covers the city of London. Plunging into the
gulf of black mist as if into the mouths of Tartarus, I crossed
the town. . ."

There were other smoky places too, some of them surprisingly so. When Juan Rodriguez Cabrillo of Portugal discovered California in 1542, he found a pall already over the area. The smoke from Indian campfires rose only a short distance and then spread like a ceiling over the valley in back of San Pedro Bay, near what is now Los Angeles. And the Indians had another name for the bay—they called it the "Bay of Smokes."

When settlers began to build a new nation in America, it was generally a haven of clean air and clean water. But industry soon arrived, and factory smoke began to darken the skies in some areas. Sawmills and industrial plants dumped increasing amounts of waste into streams. Fertilizers and new chemicals and metals began to pollute the environment. And more than a century ago a new fuel was added to the polluter's arsenal; in August of 1859, Edwin Drake dug the world's first oil well at Titusville, Pennsylvania. Here was a Pandora's Box of pollution for sure. Oil made possible almost unlimited amounts of energy for factories and later for transportation, but it also contributed, almost invisibly at first, to the pollution of our environment.

Pollution was not all invisible, of course, and Americans were aware of the problem a century and more ago. An example was the Clean Rivers and Harbors Act of 1899, the first federal legislation making water pollution illegal. It has not worked too well, as anyone can see by checking our rivers and harbors.

The Unheeded Warnings

Our concerned forefathers wrote numerous articles on pollution. The following are typical titles on the subject:

"Apparatus for Filtering Air and Smoke," *Scientific American*, May 12, 1900.

"Smoke Prevention and Public Health," *Engineering Monthly*, June, 1900.

"Pollution of Lakes and Rivers," *Outlook*, September 24, 1910.

"Stopping River Pollution," *Collier's*, November 11, 1911.

"Control of Stream Pollution," *American City*, January, 1914.

"Pathology of Smoke Pollution: Effects on Mind and Body," *Engineering Monthly*, March, 1914.

This article appeared in *Scientific American*, February 21, 1914:

PITTSBURGH'S SMOKE BILL

Smoking is a costly habit, whether the smoker happens to be a man or a town. Persons who have hitherto regarded the "smoke nuisance" as mainly an esthetic problem will be startled by revelations of Mr. J. J. O'Connor, Jr., who has been investigating the smoke of Pittsburgh from the practical viewpoint of dollars and cents. . . .

The total bill foots up $9,944,750 per annum; and no attempt has been made to include such items as depreciation in the value of property, absence of various industries which are practically excluded by a smoky atmosphere, and, last but not least, injury to human health.

Half a century ago, those concerned about pollution also cited two key factors involved: the need for civic action, and the seeming inability to take that action. The following articles are from the journal, *The American City*, December, 1923, and July, 1924, respectively:

THE SMOKE NUISANCE
A CIVIC RATHER THAN AN ENGINEERING PROBLEM

Experience has shown that the problem of smoke abatement is not so much an engineering as a psychological one. Until the public demands smoke abatement, and shows a continued interest in it, no permanent improvement is possible. Civic organizations and other interested bodies can therefore take an important part in the movement . . . by helping to stimulate public interest in the subject. The smoke abatement problem is not one that can be settled overnight and then left to take care of itself without further attention, but is something that must be watched year in and year out if high standards are to be maintained.

STREAM POLLUTION BY INDUSTRIAL WASTES AND ITS CONTROL

Reams of paper have been used in describing stream pollution, its evils and its remedies. Commissions and boards have been appointed, have investigated, and have compiled voluminous reports which have been forgotten, covered with dust, on the upper shelves of libraries or in vaults; and still, pollution in the aggregate continues to increase.

The reports piled up as the problem worsened. Belgium's Meuse Valley is a highly industrialized area along the Meuse River, and in 1911 the inevitable happened: an "inversion" held polluted air over the valley long enough to kill scores of victims. A similar disaster occurred there in the winter of 1930 during which about 6,000 were taken ill, and sixty-three deaths were attributed to the smog.

Pollution took longer to catch up with us in the United States. But in 1948 smog hung over the industrial city of Donora, Pennsylvania, and almost half of its residents became ill with chest pains, headaches, vomiting, and nausea, plus irritation of the eyes, nose, and throat. Twenty deaths were credited to the killer smog. Five years later New York City suffered an even worse pollution tragedy. Several days of smog in November, 1953 sickened thousands and killed somewhere between 175 and 260 people.

In December, 1952, Evelyn's warnings took on special significance for modern England: five days of smog killed at least 4,000 Londoners! While most of the deaths were officially classed as bronchitis, pneumonia, or heart disease, victims suffered typically from shortness of breath and cyanosis, a lack of oxygen in the blood. The deadly pollution returned in 1956, taking 1,000 lives in the short span of one day. Again in 1962 it struck, killing 750.

Pollution, then, is no new problem. When the Air Pollution Control Association met in June, 1970 in St. Louis, Missouri, the convention marked the sixty-third annual meeting of the organization. For at least seven centuries man has been aware of pollution's dangers, and stiff penalties have been enforced occasionally.

No Polluter Is An Island

There have always been industries that are detrimental to health. A mine environment may be filled with particles that cause silicosis, for example. Smelter and foundry workers breathe air that is contaminated. Workers with phosphorescent and radioactive paints have died, as have X-ray and other radiation technicians. These occupational hazards are tragic, but special precautions against them have been developed through the years. Harder to grasp is the fact that a mine, which admittedly endangers its workers, is also endangering people who have never been in the mine or even seen it, and who live dozens or hundreds of miles away.

For centuries the idea prevailed that all the millions of cubic miles of air and of ocean were vast dumps into which we could throw our garbage, sewage, and poisons. There are many who still cling to this notion. What harm can it do to burn some trash in a backyard, or a few old tires to keep an orchard warm during a freeze? How could it possibly hurt someone across the ocean if we test a nuclear bomb, or spray a field with a pesticide? John Donne noted that no man is an island. It is just as true that no human activity takes place in a vacuum. As ecologist Garrett Hardin has put it, we can't do "just one thing."

Pollution is not a personal problem or a community problem. It is not just a county or state, or even a national problem. Because of the nature of the environment, because the wind and water seldom respect political or national boundaries, pollution is a universal concern. While politically we are still years away from unity, environmentally we are and have always been one world—the only world we have. "Spaceship earth" has always been a reality but as it becomes more and more crowded with passengers, and as those passengers insist on smogging the air and poisoning the waterways and the land, the congestion is becoming more noticeable, sometimes even unbearable.

There was a time when we could get away with polluting the environment. There was a time more recently when the practice was merely a calculated risk with minimal penalties. But that time is gone. Man must begin to clean up his mess or perish in it.

3

THE DIRTY AIR

For air pollution threatens not only man's wallet and his health. Air pollution erodes his soul. Every mountain blacked out by pollution, every flower withered by smog, every sweet-smelling countryside poisoned by foul odors destroys a bit of man's union with nature and leaves his spirit diminished by the loss.

Air Pollution Primer
published by the National
Tuberculosis and Respiratory
Disease Association

Mention pollution and most people think of smog, the choking air pollution that shrouds much of the land. Not just because air pollution is the most visible of the various pollutions is it number one, however. Air is our most precious and immediately needed commodity. Man can live about five weeks without food, about five days without water. He can live only five *minutes* without air.

If food is tainted or even unappetizing, we can put off eating. Water that is off-color or has a bad smell seldom has to be drunk. But if we don't like the air we are breathing we have little choice. The best among us can hold our breaths a minute or so; after that we are in trouble. We can't postpone breathing until the air suits us.

Atmosphere: The Thin Skin of Earth

The mixture of gases we call air consists of about seventy-eight percent nitrogen, about twenty-one percent oxygen, and something less than one percent argon, with the remaining 0.04 percent made up of carbon dioxide, water vapor and a number of rare gases such as neon, helium, methane, hydrogen, ozone, nitrous oxide, carbon monoxide, xenon, and radon. It is oxygen that is vital to us, since this is the gas that "burns" the fuel in our bodies to provide us with energy. Nitrogen, which is an excellent fertilizer by the way, is important since it prevents the air from being combustible.

The atmosphere has not always been in its present form. In the early days it included ammonia, hydrogen, helium, methane, nitrogen, and a number of compounds such as hydrogen sulfide, hydrogen fluoride, hydrogen bromide, and so on in greater quantities. Some of these gradually escaped from the earth into space and some were replaced by carbon dioxide and water vapor. It is thought that the first life developed in an atmosphere of ammonia, methane, hydrogen, nitrogen, carbon dioxide, and water vapor. There was little or no oxygen present. Surprisingly, it was pollution of the atmosphere by living things, the production of metabolic waste products, that put oxygen in the air. There still exists a "purple sulfur" bacteria, which does not require oxygen

Not a cloud in the sky—except clouds of smoke. Chicago suffers when temperature inversions hold industrial pollution close to the earth's surface. —ARGONNE NATIONAL LABORATORY

'NO THANKS, I QUIT CIGARETTES... TOO MUCH OF A HEALTH HAZARD!'
—PAUL CONRAD, THE DENVER POST

for its life processes and in fact gives it off as waste. But nearly all present life forms depend on oxygen—the plants, animals, and other creatures we are familiar with.

The atmosphere serves another important purpose beyond providing us with oxygen to burn; it also helps supply us with food. Practically all we eat begins with green plants, whose chlorophyll-containing leaves have the marvelous ability to combine carbon dioxide in the air with sunlight and water to produce food in the form of carbohydrates, plus more oxygen. A single acre of forest in a year's time removes about one ton of carbon dioxide from the air, and returns in exchange about 1,500 pounds of oxygen to the atmosphere. It is estimated that all the plants in the world consume about 550 billion tons of carbon dioxide a year and produce something close to 400 billion tons of oxygen.

There has been concern of late that the amount of oxygen in the atmosphere might be decreasing since man has upset the ecological balance with pollution and by cutting back forests and other areas of vegetation. However, careful testing by the Environmental Science Services Administration indicates that the oxygen content of air has remained nearly the same as when scientists began recording it. We should keep in mind, nevertheless, the great importance of the atmosphere not only to man but also to the plants that keep him alive.

Man has lived for a long time in an atmosphere about the same as that of today and so we are adapted to this natural or "benign" atmosphere. As noted in Chapter 2, there are particles of foreign matter in the air, some of which are put there by nature. An example is pollen, which from time to time plagues many of us. Millions in the United States suffer from asthma, bronchitis, catarrh, hay fever, sinus trouble, and other problems brought on or aggravated by air-borne pollen. Other natural pollutants in the air include bacteria and fungi, some of which carry diseases far more dangerous than a mere nuisance to the allergic. Anthrax and cryptococcosis are examples of air-borne diseases which are spread without man's help.

The air is also naturally polluted with smoke, dust, and odors caused by nature. Volcanoes, storms, and fires contribute their share of these nuisances. Despite all these naturally induced pollutants, however, the atmosphere before man began to pollute it with his "unnatural" activities must have been a dream of Technicolor-blue skies and crystal, sparkling air.

Pollution and the Weatherman

It has been pointed out, tongue-in-cheek, that if there were no atmosphere there would be no air pollution problem. It is tempting to name unfavorable weather as the real culprit. There are days in Arizona when one can see for eighty-five miles in the vicinity of a copper smelter. Because of meteorological conditions, much of the time the air is clear or even sparkling in pollution problem areas.

Everyone must put up with a certain amount of pollution as the price of having air to breathe. And the situation could be far worse. If the air remained still the pollution problem would be compounded dangerously. Air masses do temporarily hang motionless over certain areas, but fortunately, the atmosphere is generally in constant motion.

Unlike the moon, the earth has an atmosphere and also rotates, which is good for many reasons. If the moon did have an envelope of air surrounding it, it might still be a miserable place to live. But the earth's rotation sets up air movements we call wind. The sun helps, too, by unevenly heating land and water and thus producing other air movements including those in a vertical direction. The combination of horizontal wind and vertically moving "convection" currents tends to stir the atmosphere and mix whatever pollutants are in it. If this mixing were complete and the pollutants evenly distributed through all the billions of of billions of tons of air, we could breathe much easier for many centuries to come. But unfortunately the mixing is far from perfect.

We noted that in the early days of the earth's development some of the gases escaped from the pull of gravity and left the atmosphere permanently for outer space. This suggests a wonderful solution to the pollution problem— simply let all the pollutants depart from the atmosphere! This solution must remain in a class with the wonderful and unattainable perpetual-motion machine. Gravity holds pollutants but it also holds the good air; we must put up with one to get the other. Perhaps the only way to make use of outer space as a cosmic dumping ground is to launch capsules of waste from Cape Kennedy or some other rocket port. Interestingly, such a solution has been suggested for "hot" radioactive waste. As yet this expensive garbage disposal system has not been put into operation and probably never will be, but it is an intriguing idea.

Although the atmosphere extends as high as fifty miles (it is very, very thin at that point) most pollutants remain much closer to earth because of their weight and the fact that there is little to carry them higher against the continuing pull of gravity. Most pollutants never climb higher than two miles. Many don't get higher than a few hundred feet.

The movement of air over the earth is not a simple, easily explained or diagrammed process. In fact meteorology is among the most complex of the sciences. In addition to the rotation of the earth there is the "Coriolis effect" that causes an air mass to curve as it moves north or south. Variation in pressure causes movement of air masses, and this movement produces wind. The surface of the earth has an obvious effect on air movement, with its variety of smooth and rough places, its slopes and flats, its water and its land. High in the atmosphere the fast-moving "jet streams" that can boost the speed of airplanes by more than a hundred miles an hour also have an effect on weather. These jet streams may be influenced by the interaction of solar radiation with the magnetic fields that surround the earth. So the great mixing kettle of the atmosphere is not easy to trace or to predict. We can only say with certainty that it is extremely variable.

Much work has been done toward control of the weather, and some small successes seem to have been obtained. Perhaps the day will come when, in addition to controlling wind, precipitation, and temperature, man can also minimize pollutants by mixing them smoothly and evenly into the billions of tons of air so that no one area will suffer all the bad effects.

A number of physical phenomena aid in spreading pollution evenly through the air. The motion of an air mass simply carries the smoke or other pollutants downwind; this takes it away from the polluter but carries it to where it may bother or endanger others. The process called diffusion is also taking place with the help of a molecular action known as the Brownian movement. The same principle can be seen when sugar is left alone in a cup of coffee; in time it will diffuse by itself. This same diffusion occurs in the atmosphere when small local movements of air, and also of the individual molecules of air, stir and mix pollutants.

There are also phenomena that work against the mixing and dissipating of pollutants. The "temperature inversion" is the chief villain here; such inversions have plagued Los

Angeles, New York, London, and a host of other places.
Normally the air temperature decreases in higher attitudes.
But sometimes, because of weather frontal activity, for
example, the air high above the ground may be warmer.
This inversion discourages the tendency of air to rise ver-
tically as it does under normal, or "convective" conditions.
Combine an inversion with a valley, or an area surrounded
by high ground, and a bad pollution situation exists.

Concerned but unscientific citizens have suggested boring
holes through the hills east of Los Angeles to let the smog
flow through with the prevailing winds, or installing huge
fans to do the job. These solutions are similar to the proposal
of transporting pollutants to outer space; there just isn't
enough money available to build the fans or dig the tunnels
that would be needed. And even if such plans were carried
out the result might be simply to move the mess into someone else's back yard.

Our Aerial Garbage

Surprisingly enough, air is quite heavy; a small roomful
weighs more than a hundred pounds. Although it weighs only
about one millionth as much as the earth, the atmosphere
presses down with a weight of more than five million billion
tons! If we divide the total amount of air by the number of
humans on the globe we get the per capita share of each.
This comes to almost one and one-half million tons of air
per person. Since we each breathe only about thirty-five
pounds of air a day, it would seem that each of us has a
generous supply. But such calculations are deceptive. In the
first place they are average figures which assume that people
are evenly distributed over the surface of the earth, which of
course they are not. As people congregate in large cities, the

air ration dwindles. As the population of earth grows (and it is doubling about every thirty-five years now) this too cuts our share. Crucial to the whole calculation is the proportion of pollutants in the "pure air," a percentage that is increasing appreciably.

Soot still blackens cave walls where early man lived tens of thousands of years ago, so smoke must have been a local problem even then. But wood smoke is little more than a nuisance that dims the view, burns the eyes, and smudges skin and clothes. It falls into the same category as the odor pollution caused by sewers and found in some of the "undesirable" trades such as embalming and the tanning of leather. Such air pollution wrinkled noses and made life miserable but was not particularly dangerous to health.

Coal changed the smoke situation by adding sulfur pollutants to the air. The chemical industry made things worse by pumping increasing amounts of hydrochloric acid, hydrogen fluoride, zinc, lead, arsenic, and so on into the atmosphere. After coal came the fossil fuels of oil and gas. And added to those are the dust and dirt and other particle contaminants that are released into the air from heavy industries.

There is an old saying that each of us will eat a peck of dirt before we die. It is statistical fact that every year each of us *breathes* about one and a half pounds of dirt in the form of dust particles. The body handles this in a variety of ways. Some dirt is filtered out by the nose or washed into the stomach and from there into the intestines for elimination. Some, of course, gets into the lungs. This amount of "honest" dirt would be bad enough. But what of cement dust, carbon black, mercury, arsenic, and so on? Once such air poisoning was confined to those who worked in certain industries. Now these pollutants are being broadcast for all to share.

Cigarettes are considered so dangerous that the government (which subsidizes the tobacco industry and also collects taxes on its products!) requires manufacturers to print warnings on cigarette packs. And what of the smoke that even the non-smoker must breathe when he is in a building or bus or plane with smokers? One hundred parts per million of carbon monoxide triggers a smog alert in some communities. Cigarette smoke has 40,000 parts of carbon monoxide per million.

Name Your Poison

All air pollutants are either particulates or gases. Particulates are not only solid particles, but liquid as well. Large particles ease the pollution problem by settling rapidly out of the air. Coarse dust and ash are examples. Smoke is made up of solid or liquid particles smaller than one micron (about 1/25,000th of an inch) in diameter. Particles this small are usually called aerosols since they remain suspended in the air much as gases do. The major pollutants and their contributions to total air pollution are:

Carbon monoxide	50%
Sulfur oxides	18%
Hydrocarbons	13%
Nitrogen oxides	8%
Particulate matter	8%
Others	3%

The list of air pollutants goes from aeroallergens to zinc. Among the "miscellaneous pollutants" are fluorides, oxidants, ozone, peroxyacetylnitrate, aldehydes, lead, beryllium, arsenic, asbestos, pesticides, fungicides, and herbicides containing kerosene, sulfur, copper sulfate, and cyanide.

Although *carbon monoxide* accounts for a large share of the total pollution and is a dangerous and highly toxic gas, few deaths can be traced directly to it, and its effects are uncertain. Elemental carbon causes soot, which is not just a nuisance but also a possible carrier of hydrocarbons that may produce cancer. Carbon dioxide (into which carbon monoxide probably changes after several days) is necessary in proper amounts for plant photosynthesis, and it is not generally classified as a pollutant. However, when moisture is present, CO_2 can change to carbonic acid and as such is responsible for eroding stone and corroding magnesium and other metals. Cleopatra's Needle, a priceless stone obelisk brought from Egypt to New York, has suffered more erosion from its ninety years in our smog than during its 3,500 years in Egypt. It has rightly been called "a sad monument to air pollution."

Sulfur compounds are the most harmful of the major pollutants. Joining with oxygen in the air, sulfur from coal and fuel oils produces sulfur oxides, which can combine with water vapor and produce sulfurous acid. This in turn can join with oxygen to produce sulfuric acid, not a pleasant substance to have in our throats and lungs. Besides injuring humans, sulfur oxides harm plants, erode metals, and dissolve marble.

There are a variety of *hydrocarbons* that pollute the air, including olefins and aromatics. Olefins are found in photochemical smog and aromatics include known and suspected carcinogens.

Nitrogen by itself is a harmless gas and is classified as inert. But when mixed with air it can produce nitric oxide and nitrogen dioxide. These pollutants are present only in technologically advanced countries which produce them as unwanted byproducts of industrial and other activities.

A little *fluoride* seems to be beneficial; it is used in domestic water to prevent tooth decay, for example. But the fluorides that pollute the air are too much of a good thing. They

Even Phoenix, Arizona, has its smog problem. Such a murky sky would have been unheard of a few years ago. Roadside signs create "visual" pollution, as well.

—THE ARIZONA REPUBLIC

Automotive smog is a complex problem, as this drawing shows. Exhaust pipes remain the biggest contributors, but fuel tanks and carburetors also contribute appreciable amounts of pollutants. —STANDARD OIL COMPANY OF CALIFORNIA

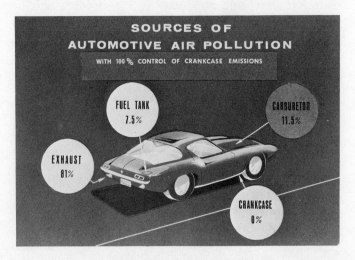

SOURCES OF
AUTOMOTIVE AIR POLLUTION
WITH 100% CONTROL OF CRANKCASE EMISSIONS

FUEL TANK
7.5%

CARBURETOR
11.5%

EXHAUST
81%

CRANKCASE
0%

This "sea" from which island mountains protrude is smelter smoke from Arizona copper mines. The mountains are the Superstitions, of Lost Dutchman gold mine fame.
—THE ARIZONA REPUBLIC

Charge this one to nature. A Gulf Coast oil tank blazes in the aftermath of a hurricane.
—NATIONAL OCEANIC AND ATMOSPHERIC ADMINISTRATION

damage vegetation and also accumulate in the tissues of animals that eat this vegetation. Man is harmed by fluorides through eye and skin irritation, inflammation of the respiratory tract, and breathing difficulties.

Some pollutants are formed in *photochemical* smog, the kind that plagues Los Angeles and other areas. Here, sunlight reacts with pollutants in the atmosphere to produce ozone, which is a special form of oxygen with three atoms per molecule instead of the normal two. Ozone is nothing like oxygen, however, and can cause choking, coughing, fatigue, and headaches. It is also harmful to fabrics and rubber, and to vegetation. Another product of photochemical reactions is PAN (peroxyacetyl nitrate), which irritates the eyes and lungs, and harms vegetation. *Aldehydes* are also formed, resulting from hydrocarbons combining with oxygen. These irritate the eyes and the respiratory tract.

Lead is also a dangerous element, and kills hundreds of people a year, mostly children who eat it in paint. It is released into the air from vehicle exhausts and also from a number of industries. Although it is thought that lead in the air is dangerous to man, little positive information is yet available and we do not know at what level of storage in the tissues lead begins to affect us. We know more about *beryllium*, used in making metal alloys. Poisoning has occurred among workers at plants using beryllium and even among people living nearby. Many fatalities have resulted. *Asbestos* has long been associated with lung disease. This pollutant is released into the air from brake linings, from insulation of various kinds, and from roofing materials.

There are many other air pollutants. Some of them are cadmium, chromium, manganese, mercury, nickel, and vanadium. Unfortunately the new and popular plastic materials can be dangerous pollutants, since some release toxic vapors when burned.

Polluters' "Who's Who"

Each year in the United States about 150 million tons of
major air pollutants are released. This staggering amount of
aerial garbage comes from many sources. The following list
shows what percentage of the total can be blamed on each:

Transportation	60%
Industry	18%
Power generation	14%
Heating	5%
Trash burning	3%

Let's look at the problem of pollution on a broad scale.
Man's activities put harmful substances into the air, from
which they are slowly removed. Rain or snow washes out
some pollutants, others settle of their own accord. Some
change chemically to harmless substances, and some are
absorbed by living creatures. What of the remaining particles? They can't escape into space, so they settle to create
polluted soil, vegetation, and water.

An obvious solution to the problem is to keep any pollutants from being released into the atmosphere. But filtering
sizable objects from the environment appears to be impossible, and air pollutants are generally tiny particles, some so
small that 50,000 of them would just make a good-sized
raindrop! Most experts say that we cannot eliminate air
pollution and that the best we can hope for is to keep it below
a dangerous level.

Combustion puts most of the pollutants in the air. This
process drives the engines that generate electrical power,
and it is a part of many industrial processes. But it is the
internal-combustion engines of our transport vehicles and
other machines that do the most harm.

When perfect combustion takes place, fuel is converted to

carbon dioxide, water vapor, heat and energy. In some processes it is possible to come close to this goal. But the burning that takes place in an internal-combustion engine is far from ideal, and complete combustion does not occur. As a result, large amounts of pollutants are released. On an average day, vehicles in the United States pump 250,000 tons of carbon monoxide, 25,000 tons of hydrocarbons, and 8,000 tons of nitrogen oxides into the air. In a year this totals about eighty-six million tons!

It is a remarkable and ironic fluke of technology that the electric car was invented before the gasoline-powered vehicle. Before Henry Ford put America on wheels with his sputtering Tin Lizzies, many pollution-free battery-powered automobiles were built and operated. But the electric car lacked the power and acceleration of the internal-combustion engine, and it quickly took a back seat.

Early cars were puny, primitive beasts, but their progeny were quickly improved. More power came from their pumping pistons, so that in time we could spin the tires, or "burn rubber," by pushing hard enough on the gas pedal. (Incidentally, tons of rubber in this form pollute the air!) Some critics say that if automobile engines had remained similar to those of the early 1900's we would not have a serious automotive pollution problem today. But of course they didn't. Higher-compression engines produced more power, but they needed something to keep them from "knocking," or pre-igniting, under a heavy load. So the additive "tetraethyl lead" was developed and blended with the gasoline. Today, particles of lead—which is highly toxic—are found practically everywhere on earth, and high in the skies as well, where they are believed by some meteorologists to be affecting the global precipitation pattern.

Industry is the second largest offender, adding twenty-five million tons of pollutants to the air yearly. A single copper smelter of moderate size can put 1,500 tons of sulfur dioxide into the atmosphere per day. Nor is the smelter the only offender on such a scale. Oil refineries, of which there are many more, emit about 450 tons. Even coal-fired power plants can put 300 tons of sulfur dioxide into the air daily.

Combustion is not the only source of air pollution, of course. Evaporation occurs with many liquids, including the gasoline in your car. One estimate puts the value of gasoline lost each year in this way at $3 billion! In industry, heat and pressure cause evaporation on an even greater scale, and some of the evaporated material escapes into the atmosphere.

"Attrition," or grinding, accounts for pollution too. When a car tire slides in stopping, or spins in making a quick start, some rubber is ground off and released into the air. Your shoes lose leather or rubber as you walk. Gravel pits produce much dust and dirt and rock particles, as do cement plants and many others by the grinding of material. Sanding of surfaces for painting, grinding, sandblasting, drilling, and polishing all add pollutants to the air, some of them far more than nuisances.

Radiation has been part of the air pollution problem for some time but with the coming of the nuclear age the problem was made far more serious. Atom bombs have shown what they can do, and accidental releases of radiation have harmed life in some areas since the war. Now the nuclear power plant has been added to the producers of pollution. This problem will be discussed in detail in Chapter 7.

After the nuclear age came the space age, ushered in by the Russian satellite Sputnik. Today we have progressed a long way from these first steps in space. Huge booster rockets propel spacecraft into orbit or deep into space, and many tons of pollutants, including some of the most deadly, remain in the atmosphere. Among the toxic pollutants ejected by rocket engines are beryllium and fluorine compounds, nitrogen tetroxide, and dimethylhydrazine. Such materials have been blamed for damage to property and to vegetation.

A single jet airliner on takeoff has been estimated to produce as much pollution as 10,000 automobiles. Pollution authorities in New York City have estimated that aircraft are to blame for about four percent of the total pollution that occurs in that area. Some scientists are concerned that SST aircraft may add so much water vapor to the upper atmosphere that they will change our weather. They have fought to stop construction of the planes. The same fear has been expressed about rocket exhaust as increasing numbers of spacecraft are launched. Even the harmless carbon dioxide from combustion may at some future date alter the earth's temperature so that ice at the poles will melt and cause flooding of many major cities. However, some scientists believe that the carbon dioxide content of the atmosphere might act to *lower* the temperature instead. Either of these eventualities is a long way off, and while we must be concerned about them, there are more pressing immediate problems stemming from air pollution.

Who Can Breathe Easily?

Late in 1970 California's Air Resources Board warned that dangerous amounts of nitrogen oxides were being released into the air. Every day, the report stated, 1,400 tons of such oxides were released over the South Coast Air Basin. In 1940 only 280 tons were released daily and the population was only a fraction of what it is at present. Pollution danger is thus mounting from two sources: more people breathing the air, and more contaminants in the air.

The Los Angeles area is not the only one in trouble. A list

prepared by the U.S. Public Health Service rated the sixty-five largest cities on three pollution factors: dust, ash, and other particles; gasoline pollutants; and sulfur dioxide. A rating of zero meant clean; 195 meant filthy air. Los Angeles-Long Beach ranked fourth in that list with a score of 393.5. New York scored first at 457.5; Chicago second at 422.0; and Philadelphia third with 404.5. Only eleven of the sixty-five cities were rated less than filthy!

Here is a list of some of the harmful effects of air pollution:

1. Ruins vegetation, flowers, crops;
2. Makes paint peel and discolor;
3. Adds to housecleaning and clothes cleaning costs;
4. Kills cattle and destroys feed;
5. Rusts iron and tarnishes silver;
6. Cracks tires, deteriorates nylon;
7. Wastes fuel in power plants;
8. Cuts down sunlight.

It is estimated that air pollution in 1970 caused about $1 billion in damage to agriculture alone. Costs resulting from illnesses add perhaps $2 billion more. In total it is believed that air pollution costs this country something like $14 billion yearly. These are amounts in dollars and do not attempt to take into consideration human suffering and loss of life. Neither can they account for accidents caused by smog or the offensive smells and sights air pollution can bring about. Many authorities feel that $14 billion is a bare minimum of what pollution costs, and that the true total is many times this amount. What price can we put on human life?

Air is our most vital requirement, and each day we breathe in some 15,000 quarts of it. Without air we would lose consciousness in little more than a minute and die in about five minutes. Suffocation must be excruciatingly horrible. But perhaps the miner whose lungs are clogged with the mineral

dust that causes silicosis fares even worse, for he suffers for
years, as do the victims of other respiratory ailments. Death
by pollution may thus be worse than the mercifully short
agony of suffocation. Cigarette packs must be labeled "hazardous to your health," since careful testing indicates that
smoking can cause death. In some of our cities today just
breathing the air is equivalent to smoking two packs of
cigarettes a day; it has been suggested ironically that signs
be posted at the city limits declaring, "Caution: the air you
breathe may be hazardous to your health."

Air pollution kills people. Lung cancer takes about 50,000
lives every year in the United States. Chronic chest diseases
kill another 80,000. As one doctor has stated, "The repeated
association of high levels of pollution with peaks in mortality
is more than coincidental."

Residents of the north shore of Staten Island in New York
City breathe the fumes from industrial areas of eastern New
Jersey. Those on the south shore breathe relatively un-
polluted air. A medical study has shown that the lung cancer
death rate among men living on the north shore is fifty-five
per 100,000 compared with forty per 100,000 for those on
the south shore. For women, the death rate from cancer is
twice as high among north shore residents as those living on
the south shore.

We are not all going to die quickly from air pollution. We
can even be encouraged by the statistics that show our
longevity increasing rather than getting shorter. But it is
later than we think and surely each breath we take is a little
worse than the last. Of all our pollution woes, air pollution is
the worst. The sooner we clean it up the easier we can breathe.

4

AND THE FILTHY WATER

> *There is no excuse for a river flowing red with
> blood from slaughterhouses. There is no
> excuse for paper mills pouring tons of sulfuric
> acid into the lakes and streams. There is no
> excuse for chemical companies and refineries
> using our major rivers as pipelines for toxic
> wastes. There is no excuse for communities to use
> the people's rivers as a dump for raw sewage.*
>
> *President Lyndon B. Johnson*
> *October, 1965*

Solid as we look, we are mostly water. More than sixty percent of our substance is water, and we must constantly replenish ourselves with more water, from one to two quarts a day in some form. Man dies without air in five minutes; his water needs are somewhat more forgiving, but in five days most of us would perish if deprived of all water. Death by thirst is probably an even worse fate than starvation, for in its last stages men become raving lunatics who may even try to bite themselves to drink their own blood.

Water, then, is vital to life, and there is a hydrologic cycle paralleling the carbon cycle in the atmosphere. Water itself is a chemical compound accurately classified as a mineral. Simpler in composition than air, water consists of just two elements, as indicated by the chemical shorthand symbol H_2O. In a molecule of water there are two atoms of hydrogen and one of oxygen. Water retains its identify and pollutants can generally be removed without any irreversible changes in its composition.

We noted that there are millions of billions of tons of air in the atmosphere. There are 327,672,000 *cubic miles* of water on the earth. Slightly more than ninety-seven percent of this water is in the oceans and somewhat more than two percent is frozen in polar ice caps and in glaciers. This leaves less than one percent for all the lakes, rivers, streams, and "aquifers" or underground reservoirs. Thus nearly all the earth's water is salty and unfit to drink. However, even one percent of 327 million cubic miles is an appreciable amount of water, and on a proportionate basis, every human on earth has about a hundred million gallons of fresh water as his share.

Just as the air is in constant motion, so the waters of the earth are seldom still. Each year some 95,000 cubic miles of water evaporate into the atmosphere as water vapor. Every year 71,000 cubic miles of this total returns to the oceans as rain or snow; 15,000 cubic miles of it falls on the earth to nourish living things. The remaining 9,000 cubic miles falls on or runs into lakes and rivers. Practically all water eventually finds its way back to the sea.

French scientist Antoine Lavoisier in 1776 succinctly described nature's pollution of sea water: "Sea water results from the rinsing of the whole surface of the earth." This rinsing results in nearly all the elements being found in the sea—in fact, two elements, iodine and bromine, were first

THE HYDROLOGIC CYCLE

It's the same water, constantly recycled in nature's vast hydrologic cycle. Man must begin to look for shortcuts to this recycling process."
—ENVIRONMENTAL PROTECTION AGENCY

discovered there. Two radioisotopes, silicon 32 and beryllium 10, were also found first in the sea.

The oceans are sometimes described as a three percent solution of salts, but this does not do justice to the variety of elements therein. For example, gold is found there. The renowned German chemist Fritz Haber spent many years trying to extract it profitably to save his country from economic ruin following World War I. He was not successful, but the sea is mined profitably for some other minerals. Salt is the most used of these, and each year some 350 million tons of it are extracted. More than 100,000 tons of bromine, 106,000 tons of magnesium, and almost 700,000 tons of metal compounds are also taken from the sea annually. Surprisingly, however, it is fresh water that is second in the quantity extracted from the sea—more than 140 million tons a year.

When we place man alongside 327 million cubic miles of water, he seems insignificant as a polluter of the oceans. Neither has he had the eons of time that nature has, during which she scoured the elements from the land and washed them into the sea. Yet man is already more than matching nature as a water polluter in some regards.

Is There Really *A Water Pollution Problem?*

We should be greatly concerned about water pollution. Aside from the recreational and esthetic pleasures of our many waterways, there is also the fact that much food comes from the sea. For a world faced with the problem of food shortages, the sea catch provides an appreciable amount of our protein needs. Water is also necessary for drinking and other domestic uses, for industry, and for farming. There was a time when there were so few people producing so little pollution that man's muddying of the waters was not worth worrying about. Those days are long gone. Man has managed to turn his waterways into such sinks of pollution that they kill the marine life in them, and sometimes even burst into flames.

Our major rivers no longer contain just water, but a list of substances that reads like a dictionary. Mercury and other chemical poisons kill fish. Sewage contains communicable disease bacteria. Farmers wash dirt, fertilizer, and pesticides into our water supply, and radioactive fallout settles into it. Hot water "thermally" pollutes it so that not only do animals and organisms die in it, but *the river loses vital oxygen and also "dies."* So do lakes, as studies of Lake Erie show. You can make a "study" even if you aren't a scientist: just read the signs that warn against swimming in a lake because it is dangerously polluted. The Potomac River is contaminated too, disgracing our nation's capitol. So are the Hudson River, Lake Geneva and Lake Constance in Switzerland, Russian rivers and lakes, and the famous Thames River in England. Even the Scandinavian countries, the last we would think of as suffering from pollution, are beginning to see their fjords dirtied, and black snow falls from their skies. Signs implore visitors not to litter and pollute the way they do back home.

Wasteful practices are part of the problem. The United States in particular is noted for its consumption of natural resources, fresh water included. Congressional pollution hearings turned up the interesting fact that while Swedish washing machines are designed to use about five gallons of water per load of wash, our machines require seventeen gallons. For a given amount of domestic wastes European sewage systems use fifty gallons of water but for the same amount of wastes we use a hundred gallons. There are two sides to this argument, of course. By using more water, we produce an effluent less concentrated with pollutants and easier to clean up. But we also use far more water, and this compounds the problems of pollution and shortage.

In our West and Southwest, greatly increasing demands have resulted in "mining" water from the ground, so that water tables drop and yield poorer quality, more expensive water supplies. Silt and salt contaminate water. The Great Lakes and many other areas are faced with the destruction of marine life and the desecration of beaches by sewage discharge and industrial chemicals. Lake Erie, an all-too-typical example, has been described as a "giant chemical vat" rather than a natural body of water. Pesticides and insecticides run off farmland and pollute waterways. Industrial wastes, principally in the East, have fouled rivers and estuaries and destroyed fish and shell-fish industries.

Water shortages in desert areas are to be expected but we have recently experienced critical shortages even in our rainy Northeast. As with air pollution, the problem is two-fold. First, we have more people, each of them using more water than ever before in our history. (On a per capita basis we use more than 15,000 gallons per day!) Second, we are putting an ever-greater pollution load on the water. As a result, there are proposals for nuclear or other artificial desalination devices for coastal waters.

Nature, in the form of rainfall and snowfall, distills water free and makes the job seem easy. However, engineers have learned that desalting is *not* easy and it is far from cheap. Studies of a projected fuel-fired desalinating plant in California showed that it would require practically all the natural gas available in the area! Even nuclear-powered plants would produce water with a very high price tag—a commodity once thought of as almost free. A seldom-considered part of the price is transportation. To deliver desalted sea water any distance would cost so much that neither farmers nor industry could afford it.

Man Gets Into the Act

We pollute water in many different ways. We dump solid wastes into it. We add organic wastes, some of them with a potential for causing disease. We introduce hundreds of chemical compounds to the water, many of these toxic or otherwise damaging to man or the environment. And we add heat, which is of great harm to life in the water—life we may depend on for food or at least for pure water. The oxygen content of water is important in its ability to sustain marine life, and also to purify itself of pollutants. Heated water loses oxygen, and at the same time makes the life in it demand more oxygen. Biological Oxygen Demand, or B.O.D., is a most important term for the water pollution engineer.

Domestic sewage is only part of water pollution. Industry contributes an equally large share, dumping organic material, chemicals, dirt, and inorganic wastes into streams. Industry and power plants also pollute the water thermally. Power generation is accomplished by combustion, and since no heat engine is more than forty percent efficient, at least sixty percent of the heat produced by fuel is waste heat.

Surprisingly, nuclear power plants make the thermal pollution situation worse instead of better. Although nuclear power is competitive in price, present atomic power plants waste twice as much heat as old-fashioned conventional-fuel plants. It is estimated that by the year 2000, twenty percent of our *total* water supply will be used just to cool power plants. This water, warmed as much as twenty degrees, will have a drastic effect on marine life.

Mines pollute the atmosphere with sulfur dioxide and other pollutants from smelter stacks. Mines are also major polluters of streams through acid drainage. Even long-abandoned mines continue to contaminate the water with

*This garbage dump was created by fishermen near Irvine, Kentucky.
Such thoughtlessness is a big factor in the pollution problem.*
—U. S. DEPARTMENT OF AGRICULTURE

*Many industries locate on waterways because it is convenient to dump
wastes into them, as shown here.* —U. S. DEPARTMENT OF AGRICULTURE

colorful "Yellow Boy" discharges, as ground water filters through pyrites, or "fool's gold," deposits in the earth. In abandoned mines, little or no effort is made to check acid drainage. It is difficult and in some cases seems impossible to combat the problem.

Even with the best intentions, we compound the problems of pollution. Back in the 1930's the garbage disposal unit was invented and marketed for installation in kitchen sinks. At first glance here was a boon to mankind. No more wet, smelly sacks of the stuff to carry. No more mess to attract pests and breed disease in the alley or alongside the house. The only people to suffer would seem to be those who earned a living hauling away garbage or perhaps feeding it to animals. Yet, as perceptive critics were quick to point out, even as the electric "hogs" were being publicized, a new threat had come to our waterways. We were taking garbage out of one pocket and putting it in the other. The town dump would be cleaner—but the river would become a cesspool. It did, as we now know.

There is an even more ironic paradox in the great laundry problem. When German chemists devised synthetic substitutes for natural soaps during World War II, the discovery was hailed as one of the few good things for which Adolph Hitler was responsible. America was quick to adopt the new detergents, which seemed to clean better than soap.

Yet in a few years we had water pollution that no one had ever dreamed possible.

Mountains of detergent billows clogged our waterworks. Persistent, inorganic chemicals remained in the water despite all attempts by sanitary engineers to remove them. Before detergents, nature had cleaned the water with bacteria. Natural soaps had been "biodegradable"; that is, they broke down on exposure to bacteria. Unfortunately, the new detergents did not.

The muck seeping from this abandoned mine in West Virginia is acid. Sadly, there are about 20,000 such pollution sources in our country today. —ENVIRONMENTAL PROTECTION AGENCY

Mountains of detergent suds—and they last practically forever! This pollution problem is about solved, but phosphates now pose an even greater one. —U. S. DEPARTMENT OF AGRICULTURE

Over a period of years the problem was solved—or so it was thought. Spending a fortune in research, soap makers devised high-cleaning detergents with phosphate constituents. But an even worse problem appeared, for phosphates cause some marine life to grow prodigiously and choke out more beneficial types. Phosphates are blamed for turning Lake Erie into a chemical vat in which commercial species of fish have died off and been replaced by "trash" fish. And good plant life has been replaced by monstrous seaweeds that choke out all else. So, in trying to keep clean, we have also succeeded in polluting our water—a result that could only be achieved with the miracles of modern chemistry!

Many groups, including Congress, are attempting to forbid the use of phosphates in soaps. Soap manufacturers, however, claim that this will result in inefficient cleaning of our laundry, dishes, and so on. They prefer that we remove the phosphates in our waterworks if removal is necessary. Many of them also point out that other sources have been contributing phosphates to our waters for years, and elimination of all soap phosphates will not solve the problem.

Lead and mercury are of great concern today as pollutants, and man rivals nature in adding these to the water. When tetraethyl lead was introduced as an "anti-knock" constituent of gasoline in 1925, there was about 0.01 to 0.02 microgram of lead per kilogram of seawater. This contaminating mineral had been washed from the earth by rivers and deposited naturally in the oceans. Today there is about 0.07 microgram per kilogram in the sea water; man has succeeded in more than tripling the amount of lead in the water in just a few decades!

Each year the rains and rivers "rinse" about 5,000 tons of mercury from the land and carry it to the sea. But man, using mercury in many of his industrial processes, releases perhaps 4,500 tons into the environment yearly, and much or most of it probably ends up in the oceans. Mercury has already demonstrated its deadly effects in Japan, where mercury wastes from an acetaldehyde plant were dumped into bay waters and contaminated the fish. The result was mercury poisoning dubbed the "Minimata Bay Disease," which has killed forty-one Japanese. And mercury pollution of waters here in the U. S. has increased alarmingly.

Oil spills are much in the news, as they should be. On the average, about one million tons of petroleum are leaked or spilled into the waters of the world each year. Although this is only about one-tenth of one percent of all oil carried in tankers, it is an appreciable amount. Catastrophes like the grounding of the tanker *Torrey Canyon* in the English Channel and the Santa Barbara offshore well leaks in 1969 have dumped as much as 100,000 tons of petroleum into a relatively small area of water.

As mentioned earlier in this chapter, there are naturally occurring radioisotopes in the oceans. But man has put radioactive substances there too. Our Atomic Energy Commission has released substantial amounts of radioactive materials into the Columbia River at Richland; England's Atomic Energy Authority has done the same thing at Windscale, on the Irish Sea. Bomb tests have introduced pollutants too, and strontium 90, cesium 137, carbon 14, chromium 51, cobalt 60, and zinc 65 are now present in measurable quantities in the oceans. Government agencies believe that amounts of radioactive pollution are still far below dangerous levels, however. In fact, radioactive nuclides are often used as "tracers" to study the movements of water.

Scottish scientists in 1865 made an odd and momentous discovery. Although they could not detect the presence of barium, copper, cobalt, lead, nickel, and zinc in sea water, they did find measurable amounts in sea creatures. The answer to this riddle is that fish or other marine life concentrate the pollutants, acting much like filters, or sponges, to soak up tiny amounts until they become appreciable. Today this same effect is noted in the concentration of DDT in fish. Canned mackerel was taken off the market in California in 1969 because the fish contained pesticide residue in excess of what the Food and Drug Administration considered to be safe. Mercury-contaminated canned tuna was found in 1970. This unhappy phenomenon compounds the problem of water pollution and seems to present an ever-increasing threat from the environment we are helping create.

Nature's Sewer

Dr. Lee DuBridge, President Nixon's former science advisor, made this comment on pollution:

> The oceans of the world are so vast in size and volume that it would take an inconceivable amount of waste products to make them into cesspools. Furthermore, natural processes go on in the ocean—processes of oxidation and processes caused by the plant and animal life in the ocean—which degrade most waste products, even including oil, into relatively harmless forms.

More recently, Dr. Edward D. Goldberg of Scripps Institution of Oceanography at San Diego, California, wrote that "the oceans of the world may be the ultimate repository for the metabolic discharges of society."

The practice of using water to carry off our wastes is historic, inevitable, and basically sound. What better way of getting rid of undesirable material? Nature has the ability to purify water quickly, and to convert offensive material into something that is neither a health nor an esthetic problem. Surely the ocean deeps represent the largest and most remote dumping grounds available to man. The controversial dumping of nerve gas into the sea was permitted only because the waters were the safest place for such dangerous material.

Even though the use of waterways as sewers has worked in years past, however, man's increasing population and advancing technology has begun to severely strain nature's ability to clean up the mess. Primitive peoples generally developed a healthy respect for their water supply which minimized nuisance and disease and supplied fresh and reasonably pure water for domestic and other purposes. Pollution of a stream was rightly considered a serious crime and there were properly severe punishments. But the press of population and the growth of polluting industries have changed the situation. Where once a million people lived "in tune with nature" on the North American continent, some 206 million of us now crowd that same area. The result is a very real water crisis, with our rivers and lakes serving as drinking water and sewers for 100 million people.

Advancing technology is a big part of the water pollution problem. At one time the major concern of domestic waterworks was to kill disease-causing bacteria. While there is still an occasional outbreak of water-borne disease, this problem is largely under control. But today there are hundreds of chemicals dumped into our water, and hundreds more of new compounds coming along each year. Removing these is a strain on waterworks as well as on the ingenuity of sanitary engineers.

While it might be desirable to have a global garbage disposal system in which all pollutants found their way to the remote bottom of the sea, it would be difficult if not impossible to achieve such a dream. Instead, it appears that there will be many much smaller hydrological cycles in numerous areas of the world, each repeating on a very small scale what nature has been doing globally since time began. Of course there will be wastes in solid form to be disposed of locally, but it has been shown that these often can be put to a good use. In areas where land has been scarred by mining operations, sludge from sewage filtration plants is hauled or pumped to the site to fertilize the ground so that vegetation will quickly heal the scars and restore the environment to beauty and usefulness.

Man Must Help Too

Many big cities are built on or near large waterways for good reason. Cities at some distance from such natural resources have difficult problems with domestic and industrial water supplies and sewage disposal. For years we managed by simply dumping wastes into the water. Slowly it became necessary to purify water for domestic purposes.

There are two approaches to water sanitation. One is to treat the water before use. This is the simpler, more sensible method. Early waterworks killed germs in the fresh-water supply and removed color and odor as best they could. Waste was dumped into whatever waterway was available. All well and good—except for those unfortunates downstream. In time it became difficult, expensive, and nearly impossible to clean up the dirty water. So we began to use the second approach: clean up the waste water before it goes back into the circulating supply. While this method is generally accepted today, it was a difficult concept to sell years ago. To many taxpayers it seemed unnecessary and certainly too expensive.

Today some of our communities, though not nearly all, treat intake water and waste water as well, but in many cases this is a token gesture. "Primary" treatment filters out the sticks and trash and other solid objects, and settles some of the smaller particles. This process eliminates about thirty-five percent of organic pollutants, meaning that either nature removes the rest or someone unlucky enough to be downstream must take out the other sixty-five percent. Nearly one-third of our communities do only this much for waste sewage.

"Secondary" treatment trickles the primary-treated effluent over a bed of stones, then chemically treats it to remove about ninety percent of organic pollutants. Far better than primary treatment, it is also about three times as expensive.

At present about twenty percent of our communities— more than 1,300 of them—dump raw sewage into rivers and streams! Thirty percent give only primary treatment; fifty percent of them provide secondary treatment as well. There are only a handful of highly effective "tertiary" treatment plants in operation. One, at Lake Tahoe in California, produces waste water that is practically clean enough to drink. This is a goal to be sought by more communities.

The tertiary plant does not depend on natural filtration through the soil but uses advanced physico-chemical methods to clean up the water. There is a price tag on such success, however. While the combined primary-secondary treatment costs about $.12 per thousand gallons of water, tertiary treatment costs $.30 per thousand gallons. Obviously we are going to have to adjust our ideas about the cost of water. At $.30 a thousand gallons, the amount used by each of us would cost $4.50 a day, and a family of four would run up a yearly water bill of $6,570!

There are a number of ways we can attack the problem of water pollution. Some idealists say we should simply stop pollution at the source. This dream is easier stated than accomplished, for we shall continue to produce waste, most likely in ever-increasing quantities. Much of this waste, one way or another, will find its way into our waterways.

Another approach would be to move pollutants quickly from lakes, rivers, and other waterways into the ocean, where they could be effectively diluted and would eventually sink to the bottom, where they would be of no harm in the foreseeable future. We would continue to rely on nature to provide fresh water by evaporation and rainfall, perhaps using weather modification to accomplish these goals. This approach may some day be achieved but success does not seem near at hand.

Still another approach is simply to clean up whatever water is available as we need and use it. This method has the merit of doing no more than is necessary, thus saving time and money. Or we could do the best possible job of cleaning up wastes before putting them into the water. Tertiary water treatment plants, industrial filters, and other clean-up agents fall into this category.

Re-cycling is suggested as a solution. It short-circuits the hydrologic cycle so that we don't have to wait months or years for nature to process the water and get it back to us in good condition. This closed-cycle water supply was used years ago in Chanute, Kansas, a community on the Mississippi River faced with an acute domestic water problem. Residents tolerated water that was slightly off-color and had a disagreeable odor, because they had no choice. No disease resulted and, although the cost was high, the project demonstrated that re-cycling could be accomplished on a short-term local basis.

Today we are much farther along technologically, and some very effective re-cycling methods have been demonstrated. One showplace is Santee, California, a small community faced with high water costs if available water from the city of San Diego is used. However, a favorable geo-

The variety of birds that have returned to this lagoon indicate that the water has been properly cleaned up after use in nearby refinery. This project is located at Richmond, California. —STANDARD OIL COMPANY OF CALIFORNIA

This air view of Santee, California shows reclamation of sewage water through a system of five lakes. Swimming pool is visible in lake at extreme left. Water is recycled for swimming, boating, fishing, and irrigation. —ENVIRONMENTAL PROTECTION AGENCY

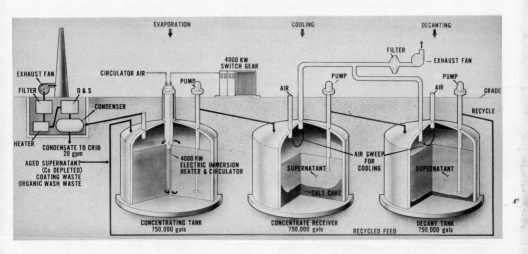

This sophisticated system reduces volume of liquid wastes from nuclear plant at Hanford, Washington. Evaporation reduces the liquid to salt cakes which are more disposable. —ATOMIC ENERGY COMMISSION
BATTELLE-NORTHWEST PHOTOGRAPHY UNIT

graphical situation allowed filtration of sewage through the soil and its return for further use. Also created in the process were an attractive boating and fishing lake and a swimming pool fed with re-cycled sewage.

Near Phoenix, Arizona, the Salt River Project reclaims sewage effluent by pumping it into settling tanks and then into the desert soil itself. Some distance away the resulting purified ground water is pumped back to the surface and used again. The project, nicknamed "Flushing Meadows," demonstrates that water can be quickly reclaimed. Although some is lost to evaporation, it will eventually be returned by nature as fresh water in the form of rain or snow. One unforeseen problem encountered at Flushing Meadows was a legal battle with the city, which claimed the effluent since it had bought and paid for the water. When a compromise was reached, development work proceeded.

The reclaiming method produces an acre-foot of water for about $5, instead of the $50 it would cost for chemical treatment. It is also more acceptable esthetically, since the percolated water is more likely to be considered "natural" ground water and not merely processed sewage. Another possibility is using waste water for fertilizer on farmland, then reclaiming the water by pumping it some distance away.

Europe's Ruhr industrial complex is often hailed by conservationists as a ray of hope. With far less water available to soak up wastes, the Ruhr River serves both as a sewer for industry and domestic wastes and as a pleasant place for boating and viewing. This has been accomplished by charging for the pollution of water; industry either cleans up waste water before returning it to the river, or pays an amount proportionate to the pollutants it introduces.

Despite some progress, we aren't out of the mud by a long way. Not when headlines tell of dangerous mercury contamination in fourteen eastern waterways. Not when ground water is being polluted with silt and salt; when beaches are closed because of filth and health hazards; and when the Department of Health, Education and Welfare reports that millions of Americans are drinking potentially dangerous water, with traces of fecal bacteria, lead, copper, iron, manganese, nitrate, arsenic, chromium, and selenium detected in many samples.

Of course, water pollution is not the critical problem that air pollution is. After all, we can go for five whole days without a drink of water.

Take your choice: a pile of unsightly old tires, or a huge billowing black cloud of acrid chemicals. —THE ARIZONA REPUBLIC

5

THE MOUNTAINS OF WASTE

*Small mountains of cardboard boxes,
rotting vegetables, papers, straw and falling
autumn leaves besmirched the city with an
unsightly mess made worse by heavy rains.
Surface rubbish had piled up at the rate of
3,000 tons daily. Sidewalks were blocked
by black plastic containers issued to housewives
and merchants to store garbage until
the strike ended. . . .
Refuse from street markets—principally in the
London areas of Petticoat Lane and Mile
End Road—posed a threat to health as enormous
piles of garbage and trash attracted rats,
flies, and disease-carrying vermin.*

U. S. News & World Report
November 16, 1970

Every day, through air and water pollution, each of us contributes about five pounds of waste to the environment. And every day each of us adds about the same amount, another five pounds, to the growing mountains of *solid* waste that some fear will soon bury us. In total, the United States is producing some 360 million tons of municipal and industrial wastes yearly, with two thirds of it coming from domestic and municipal polluters. Adding the monstrous heaps of waste from mining and other earth-moving operations, plus agricultural wastes, the total reaches three and a half *billion* tons of solid waste annually! Worse yet, the bill for this comes to about $4 billion, more than a dollar per ton for handling this useless, problem product.

The estimate for our output of goods and services in a year is about $1 trillion, so perhaps $4 billion—or four-tenths of one percent of that total—for waste handling is not a bad percentage. However, from most standpoints it *is* bad, and rapidly getting worse. Fifty years ago each of us produced about two and a half pounds of trash a day; now we produce twice that amount. We are the most consumptive society on earth; Americans, representing less than seven percent of the world's population, consume almost fifty percent of its industrial raw materials. We discard almost fifty billion metal cans a year, and more than twenty-five billion bottles. We scrap more than thirty million tons of paper and four million tons of plastic—with that last amount rising as plastic becomes more popular. And unfortunately, some plastics are very difficult and even dangerous to dispose of. Solid material extracted from sewage must also be discarded somehow. Another of the nation's eyesores is the junked automobile, and an increasing percentage of the six million scrapped each year are simply abandoned because this is the cheapest and easiest way to get rid of them. In New York City 2,500 cars were abandoned on the streets in 1960. In 1969 there were more than 50,000.

Solid wastes pose not just one problem but many, all of them important to us. First, and most obvious, is the blight of our landscapes. Smoking, stinking dumps blot out greenery and sunshine. Piles of scrapped cars ruin the scenery, with more than 17,000 automobile graveyards lining our inter-

This is one way to get rid of trash without burning it or burying it. This mess was photographed near El Paso, Texas. —U. S. DEPARTMENT OF AGRICULTURE

Solid waste in the form of scrapped automobiles is disposed of—at the price of considerable air pollution.
—THE ARIZONA REPUBLIC

state highways alone, and countless thousands elsewhere. In the last thirty years, mining operations have created huge dumps of material totaling twenty billion tons of mill tailings, slag heaps, and culm piles, hardly calculated to enhance the view or the value of surrounding land.

Not as obvious, but of even greater concern, is the threat to our health that solid waste represents. The stinking piles of garbage and the rats that are repulsive secondary evidences of solid waste pollution also harbor and spread disease. Crash programs aimed at rodent control are belated attempts to combat the real problem of wastes that attract the rats.

Another factor is cost; $4 billion is a huge sum for disposing of this solid waste, particularly when the disposal is far from satisfactory and the problem is growing every day. Only schools and highways take a larger share of municipal budgets.

Seldom considered, but in the long run a most important factor, is the waste itself. It can be argued strongly that there is no need for seven percent of Earth's people to consume almost fifty percent of its natural wealth. Cutting down on our consumption of goods would also lessen the mountainous heaps of waste. But if we can't get along on less, should we not at least strive to waste as little of our limited resources as possible? This is a major challenge of the solid waste problem—a challenge we must strive to meet.

The "Throw-away" Society

Man's fabulous productivity includes the creation of monumental piles of waste that are tributes only to his affluence and carelessness. Many people today spend more money on Christmas *wrappings* than their parents did on *presents*, only to add these wrappings to the mounting piles of trash.

'And What Do You Do With Your 'No Return' Bottles?'
—WAYNE STAYSKAL,
CHICAGO TODAY

We are a throw-away nation, pitching out boxes, cans, cartons and bottles by the billions. Rather than return containers to the store, we pay extra for the "no-deposit, no-return" variety which usually has the dubious virtue of being all but indestructible. A "tin" can is iron under its thin coating of tin, and it will rust away in a number of decades. But aluminum cans (which are lighter to carry) do not disintegrate even over a long period of time. Neither do glass bottles. Archeologists of the future may chart the course of our generation by counting and studying the containers that blight the countryside.

A recent book on pollution calls man "the dirty animal," a justifiable charge. The litterbug is a particularly disgusting example of this animal, not only producing waste but strewing it all over instead of making it inconspicuous as other animals do.

There was a time when a can or bottle was used and reused until it wore out or was broken by accident. Today only three out of one hundred are used again, the other ninety-seven being the popular throw-away, no-deposit, no-return type. Attempts to swing back to reuse of bottles by legislating higher deposits and outlawing throw-aways are often defeated through the efforts of industry lobbyists and by public apathy. Returning bottles is not only a nuisance, it seems beneath our dignity.

Twenty-five billion bottles are a problem that would seem to overshadow six million of anything. But six million automobiles, many of which contain about two tons of metal, are a problem perhaps surpassing that of the bottles and cans. It was once profitable to reuse the scrap metal in old cars for production of new steel. But when the steel companies changed to a new and improved "oxygen" process of making steel, the need for scrap declined. Indeed, it became too expensive as a rule to collect old cars, process them, and haul them to the mill to help make new steel. Fewer and fewer junked cars are reused, and more and more of them are becoming expensive white elephants and disgusting monuments to our economic system.

It does little good to complain about the situation, or to take steelmakers to task for failing to use up scrap. In a competitive economy such as ours, a manufacturer buys raw material where the price is cheapest. A well-meaning, conservation-minded mill owner could use scrap autos even though they add to the cost of his new steel, but he cannot ask a premium price because he is a nice guy doing his share for ecology and conservation. Instead, he will most likely go out of business. Would you pay $100 more for a new car just because it had a sticker on it saying "Made from old cars to save our natural resources"? Probably not many of us would.

The same situation prevails in the bottle and can business, where it is cheaper not to reclaim used metal or glass containers. After all, reusable bottles chip, and they need sterilizing and redecorating. Modern mass-production methods make new containers more cheaply than old ones can be rejuvenated. Again, why should a manufacturer penalize himself unfairly? Would you pay a premium for a beverage in a used container? Or bring your *own* container? These methods worked in the old days and they still hang on in a few isolated cases, but they are fast becoming economically unprofitable in the new "throw-away technology." The better off we become financially, the less we tend to get full use of our purchases, and the more likely we are to scrap them in favor of new replacements.

What Else Can You Do With Garbage?

In ancient times the few objects ever scrapped were left in obscure places and probably bothered no one very much. This led in time to the community dumping grounds which are still with us today and which are getting worse instead of better. Once people picked through the refuse for metal to sell as scrap, bottles, and other materials of value. But there are fewer such "rag-pickers" today, and so the dumps pile higher and higher. Dumps can add to water pollution, too, by producing acids and other drainage that contaminate streams or groundwater underlying them.

There are a number of other ways to get rid of unwanted materials and objects, however. Burning is one logical method. It reduces the volume to a fraction of the original, and in some cases it almost entirely eliminates waste, such as wood and paper. Burning leaves in the fall is an American tradition. But burning often simply shifts the pollution from solid waste to air pollution, blackening the skies and the surrounding community.

Thus far we have talked only of open burning, the kind usually done in dumps and often by homeowners, farmers, and industry. In remote areas such waste disposal might be tolerable, but rarely does such activity take place in an obscure location. A better solution is the incinerator, a structure supposedly designed for proper combustion of waste material. But while some incinerators do an excellent job most of them release great quantities of unburned material into the atmosphere, simply converting it to air pollution.

As a result of the unsanitary dump there has been a slow move toward another method of waste disposal, the "sanitary landfill." Here solid wastes are not burned at all but simply buried in trenches which hide the material and also prevent it from escaping into either the atmosphere or the water supply.

Good as the concept of the landfill is, it must be properly carried out to be successful. A survey by the government indicated that in forty states, ninety-four percent of the landfill operations were not satisfactory for a number of reasons, including water pollution danger, unplanned burning of material, and failure to cover waste material daily. Improper design and lack of attention have made many landfills anything but sanitary.

Often people who don't protest about the local dump take drastic action to prevent the creation of a sanitary landfill, if it is to be anywhere near *them*. For this reason the landfill idea is catching on only slowly. Properly used, however, it can be a double asset to a community. First, it disposes of waste with no smoke and little blight of the landscape. Even more important, it can put worthless or cheap land to a much better purpose. Often a landfill is operated for only a few years and is then developed as a park, or even for homesites. Low places may be filled in, and quite often the value of not just the landfill site but land surrounding it increases.

If solid waste can fill a hole, it can make a hill too. In fact, it has been estimated that all the solid waste produced in

California would build a wall thirty feet high and a hundred feet wide from Mexico to Oregon! Although such a massive project has yet to be built, a number of more modest "trash piles" have been erected in some areas, with the hill eventually used for such recreation as sledding and skiing slopes! Carefully engineered from both geological and sanitary disposal standpoints, a "hill of garbage" a hundred feet high topped with dirt and appropriately named Mt. Trashmore has been created in DuPage County, Illinois. It is the only high ground in the area and thus esthetically valuable for the community. It took care of wastes for several years and was designed to cause no contamination of ground waters.

Imagination has been combined with waste disposal in some communities to create such things as levees and dams. Here is a challenge for municipal leaders, engineers, sanitation experts, and others concerned with the problem to join forces and turn a handicap into an asset, to use a once worse-than-useless material in a constructive way.

Putting Garbage to Work

We have noted that incinerators traditionally have not done a proper job. A new breed of furnace is beginning to succeed, however, by burning waste of many kinds at high temperature—and even using the heat for a variety of useful purposes. Why not burn garbage and heat an apartment building or hotel at the same time, for example? This is now being done, and there are pilot incinerators in operation that convert heat to electric power. A pound of processed garbage has been found to have surprisingly high heat content, about 5,000 B.T.U.'s per pound. While this is not as much as the 10,000 to 15,000 B.T.U.'s in a pound of coal, it is appreciable. Studies indicate that properly designed incinerators could

The great American tradition of burning leaves in the fall contributes to air pollution. —MUSKEGON CHRONICLE

Another method of solid waste disposal is seen in Yargo State Park in Georgia. After this gulley is filled it will be covered over with soil. Pines will then be planted to control erosion and add to the beauty of the area. —U. S. DEPARTMENT OF AGRICULTURE

not only dispose of garbage but produce ten percent of the community's electric power needs! This would mean a further reduction in air pollution, for less fuel would be burned.

Other researchers are studying the possibility of converting garbage into protein for feeding meat animals. Scientists at Louisiana State University have turned cellulose waste into a low-cost, high-protein food. General Electric researchers are working on a similar project.

A simpler idea is the re-cycling of waste paper to produce more paper. Our forest products are an important—but definitely limited—natural resource. At one time much of the content of new paper came from old, but the current trend is toward more and more new raw material, as it is cheaper and easier to get and to use. Some ten million tons of old paper and other cellulose are used, but another thirty million tons are thrown away every year. In one city a pilot project has homeowners put paper scrap in separate containers so that it is more easily available to paper mills. Like the "garbage furnace," this method will not only conserve raw materials but subsidize the collection of garbage and thus lower the price of that service.

If paper can be put back into use, how about other kinds of waste? It is easy to list a great many types of solid waste, including the following: ashes, cloth, dirt, food, glass, leather, leaves and grass, metal, plastics, rocks, rubber, and wood.

Some waste is organic and "biodegradable." That is, it is decomposed over a period of time by bacteria. Food wastes fall into this category, as do leaves and grass, wood, and paper. Cloth and leather in time are degraded and disappear, and rubber does to some extent. But metal, glass, and plastics pose special problems.

Iron and steel rust away in time, and tin cans are broken down by the chemical action of air and water and eventually return to the soil. Aluminum is another story, and because of its light weight more and more cans and other containers are being made of aluminum. Some industries are beginning to buy scrapped aluminum cans and use them to produce more aluminum, a commendable anti-pollution effort that should be expanded.

Glass is just about everlasting, and collectors find that bottles many decades old change only by acquiring a lovely tint from the effects of the sun's ultraviolet rays. With an estimated twenty-five billion bottles going into trash cans each year, much of the solid waste piling up is glass. In Toledo, Ohio, a parking lot has been paved by Owens-Illinois Corporation, using glass mixed with asphalt, aptly called "glassphalt." Elsewhere, glass and other wastes have been utilized as the aggregate for making concrete, instead of the gravel and rock normally used.

Some attempts have been made to reclaim other useful materials from trash and garbage. Separators have been set up to extract metal, paper, glass, and so on, with these materials then gathered for sale as scrap for recycling. Unfortunately, such projects have not yet proved economically profitable, and it is obvious that unless much better handling techniques can be devised only a subsidy method can make the system work. Even high-powered scientific research funded by government grants has led to discouraging results and to the admission that at least for now this is not a promising avenue.

Hard-Core Solid Wastes

No matter what we do, how hard we try, or what we call it, some solid waste will remain just that: waste we must somehow dispose of. Increasing numbers of plastic containers are being used because this is an easy material to form in a variety of shapes. In many respects plastic is better waste than glass since it is not dangerous from the standpoint of breakage or cutting. But some of the new and popular "polyvinyl" plastics are almost impossible to get rid of. They are not biodegradable, and when burned they produce hydrogen chloride, a dangerous, highly toxic and corrosive gas. This byproduct gas is one of the major problems that must be overcome in the new high-temperature waste incinerators.

It is possible that certain packaging materials may have to be outlawed, or at least altered so that they are more easily disposed of. In Sweden research is being conducted with container material that degrades after use. Such a "self-destruct" capability would greatly aid in waste disposal and should be pursued by our industrial engineers. It is difficult to understand why a technology that produces nuclear energy, color televisions, and lunar landings can't divert some of this creative genius to the problem of packaging, which represents about thirteen percent of our waste products. A most helpful approach will be the engineering of packaging with limited life. For years industry has been accused of "planned obsolescence"; now it can plan obsolescence that will serve a useful purpose. It may be that bottles and boxes can be made to evaporate, or perhaps to dissolve in water.

Another solution to the solid waste problem is the technique of turning garbage into a liquid effluent that proceeds from the garbage disposal unit in the kitchen sink out through the plumbing. It might be possible to get rid of many more waste products from the home in this manner—crushing, grinding, or otherwise breaking them up, and possibly dissolving some in water or other liquid.

On the market, and already installed in some homes, are

"trash smashers" that compact solid waste into about one-fourth its original volume and pack the whole mess into neat, plastic-wrapped packages for disposal. About the only complaint is that the plastic bag is not biodegradable. This is not a serious shortcoming, since in a landfill it makes little difference if the material degrades or not. In fact, the plastic bag helps prevent drainage that might pollute ground water.

Better ways of shredding, baling, and otherwise handling old cars for re-cycling have been developed, and more are planned. Huge compressors squash a car into a small cube for easy handling and shipping. Other machines shred and rip junked autos into bits and pieces of convenient size. Burning techniques that remove nonmetals cheaply and quickly, yet don't pollute the air, are needed to supplant outlawed methods which accomplished the job only at the expense of clean air.

"Far-out" solutions to the solid-waste problem may help too. For example, old cars have been sunk in the sea to provide "homes" for preyed-on species of fish and other marine life, thus solving two ecological problems at once. It has been suggested that incinerators be installed in large ships; wastes could be burned and the ashes dumped far at sea where they would settle harmlessly on the ocean floor.

Not the least of our solid-waste problems is the disposal of radioactive waste, military gases or weapons, and the like. Thus far such materials have been stored in caves, sealed in metal or concrete containers and buried or sunk into the sea. The public is understandably concerned about the dangers of leakage in the future. What effect will earthquakes have on "hot" wastes stored in caves? What will leaking radioactivity do to marine life, which may in turn be eaten by humans? Perhaps radioactive waste can be put to good use, such as sterilizing stored foods against insect, rodent, and bacterial infection.

Digging Our Way Out

In 1965 the Federal Government took official cognizance of this problem by creating a Bureau of Solid Waste Management under the Department of Health, Education, and Welfare. Government planners are beginning to realize that solid wastes are a national problem even though they do not flow across the political boundaries of counties and states as do air and water pollutants.

The problem has not yet been solved. In fact, it is going to get much worse. There are now twenty-five billion bottles heaped on our dumps yearly but there will be sixty-six billion in 1980 unless some change is made. We each produce five pounds of waste a day now; we will produce eight pounds by 1980. And there will be many more of us producing our eight pounds!

Success will most likely be achieved by a combination of many approaches. Some curbs on the wasteful use of commodities are desirable. We must learn to re-cycle far more of our waste material. Better collection methods must be devised; better incineration, and, possibly, dual-use techniques producing heat or power will help.

The solid-waste problem is a big one, but not as insurmountable as all the growing mountains of waste might suggest. With hard work and intelligent planning we can rise above it.

6

THE PESTICIDE POLLUTANTS

*For the first time in the history of the world,
every human being is now subjected to
contact with dangerous chemicals, from the
moment of conception until death. In the
less than two decades of their use,
the synthetic pesticides have been so thoroughly
distributed throughout the animate and
inanimate world that they occur virtually
everywhere. . . .*

*Silent Spring
by Rachel Carson*

Most pollution is incidental or accidental waste, something
we put in the environment because we have no choice or
are careless. There are some pollutants, however, that man
consciously and purposely dumps, sprays, or otherwise introduces into the air, the water, and even his food. These are
the herbicides and pesticides, by their very nature deadly
poisons. They constitute an especially difficult segment of
the pollution problem.

A news release in late 1970 stated that rodent hairs had been found in thousands of candy bars. Disgusting as the prospect of biting into such a mess may be, there are substances in our food that pose more potential danger. Among them are such things as DDT, strontium 90 and other radioactive materials, lead, mercury, and a variety of other chemicals and pesticides.

Today there are about 900 chemical compounds used in as many as 60,000 licensed pesticides available both here and abroad. The sale of pesticide poisons produced in the U. S. in 1969 was a *$12 billion* business, compared with only $440 million in 1964! Herbicide sales increased from $200 million to $800 million during the same period.

Lake Erie, long beset by pollution that is killing it before its time, has recently been the scene of a dramatic comeback of sport fishing. The introduction of the "coho" salmon to its waters and the successful growth of these large game fish have attracted thousands to the area and touched off an epidemic of "salmon fever" among fishermen. Prospects looked good for a revival of the lake as a recreational area— until the salmon were found so contaminated with residues of the pesticide DDT that they had to be destroyed.

In Tijuana, Mexico, just across the border from San Diego, more than 500 people were made ill in 1967 from eating bread poisoned by parathion, a pesticide. Sixteen of the victims died. Six children in Fresno, California, were poisoned by new jeans that had been contaminated by the pesticide phosdrin. A long list of similar casualties has accumulated, and such tragedies will continue because pesticides are poison and as such they endanger life other than the target species they are intended to kill.

Each year in the United States about one person per million dies from pesticide poisoning, and there is a rule of thumb that indicates that for each death there are a hundred other such poisonings that are nonfatal. In light of these statistics it is easy to understand the hue and cry against DDT, and the demands by well-meaning people, including some scientists, that pesticides be banned. Why shouldn't we stop using them altogether? Unfortunately, the situation is so complicated by our need for pesticides that solutions are difficult.

In December, 1969, a commission of scientists appointed earlier by the Secretary of the Department of Health, Education, and Welfare made its report on "Pesticides and Their Relationship to Environmental Health." In that report was this introductory statement:

> The production and use of pesticides in the United States is expected to continue to grow at an annual rate of approximately fifteen percent. Predictions are that insecticides will more than double in use by 1975 and herbicides will increase at an even more accelerated pace. The foreign use of pesticides will likewise continue to increase with the organochlorine and organophosphorus insecticides continuing to represent a significant part of the foreign market.

There is good reason for the continuing and even the increased use of pesticides. The plain truth is that today we cannot live without them.

Dr. Emil M. Mrak, chairman of the commission, and Chancellor Emeritus of the University of California at Davis, put it bluntly in his letter to the Secretary of HEW: "Chemicals, including pesticides used to increase food production, are of such importance to modern life that we must learn to live with them . . . "

Indeed such chemicals are important, and although 200 or more persons die in this country each year of pesticide poisoning, there is general agreement that without pesticides *millions* would die—of disease and starvation. For man competes in the world with other species of living things, many of them predatory insects and other pests that would devastate our crops and overwhelm us with disease if we let down the bars of defense that pesticides form.

The Nature of the Pest

"Pesticide" means a killer of pests. More formally, the Commission report defines a pesticide as "a chemical used to cause the death of nonhuman organisms considered by man to be 'pests'; i.e., inimical to human interests."

Pest is a weak word for those microörganisms and other disease carriers that kill us with sickness, for the parasites that ruin our food, and for those creatures that harm us in other ways. Such dangers are not new; the Bible abounds with stories of plagues and pestilences that killed men thousands of years ago. Fighting for his life, man learned to use pesticides. One of the earliest, and one still in use, is pyrethrum, an organic compound obtained from plants. It is recorded that Marco Polo brought pyrethrum back from China and that it was hailed as a "wondrous and secret" stuff in its ability to kill insect pests. Another organic compound called red squill was used centuries ago to kill rats. A plant known as sabadilla was made into a powder that kills body lice by South Americans long ago. The tobacco plant, properly ground, was put to work in France more than two centuries ago to kill aphids; nicotine, the active ingredient, still serves this purpose in our gardens today. Petroleum, kerosene, creosote, and turpentine were used as long as two centuries ago as insecticides, particularly to kill mosquitoes.

One of the worst locust outbreaks in years occurred in 1968, affecting more than forty countries from West Africa to North India. These hordes of insects can eat their own weight each day.

—FOOD AND AGRICULTURE ORGANIZATION (U.N.)

A rice stem borer is caught in the act. Without effective control, these devastating insects can endanger the basic food supply of half the world.–THE ROCKEFELLER FOUNDATION

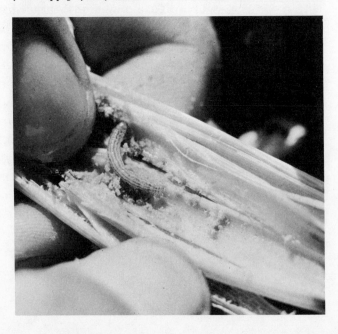

Arsenic compounds were applied as pesticides more than a century ago, and in the Rocky Mountain region one arsenic compound, known as Paris Green, prevented a potato famine. Over the years additional elements, including lead, sulfur, sodium, and many others, were added to the pesticide arsenal.

Even the "synthetic hydrocarbons," now under heavy attack by many environmentalists, are not new. These began to be developed in Germany before 1900. DDT, a chlorinated hydrocarbon, was found to be an effective insecticide in Switzerland in 1939, although the compound had been known much earlier than this. When World War II made it impossible for the United States to import such traditional organic insecticides as pyrethrum and red squill to control lice and rats, chemists turned to the synthetic compounds. DDT was one of these, and among its first achievements was the halting of a 1943 typhus epidemic in Italy almost as soon as it broke out. Since that time DDT has achieved spectacular success in drastically curbing malaria and dozens of other dangerous diseases. Coupled with this service to mankind is its use as a killer of agricultural pests. The additional food produced for the world's hungry has led some authorities to credit DDT with saving perhaps as many as 300 million lives since its introduction in 1943!

There has been much research into other methods of pest control. In 1888 the Department of Agriculture initiated biological control by importing insects to check a killing scale on citrus trees in California. More recently, dramatically successful work has been done by exposing pests to radioactive material to make them sterile. However, the Commission reports that although imaginative and exciting research is in progress, non-insecticidal control techniques are not likely to have a significant impact in the near future.

Endangered Species

Research with animals indicates that DDT is probably affecting the reproduction of some of them, that liver damage has been done, and that the shells of some birds' eggs have become thinner. These results are in addition to the outright killing of wildlife and other life forms. Environmentalists are particularly concerned about danger to "nontarget" species. Robins, for instance, were not the intended target of DDT applied to elm trees to kill the microörganisms blighting them. Nor was it the intent to kill fish or to harm marine plant life when DDT was used in farm fields or in forests. Nevertheless, run-off from fields into rivers and lakes, and other incidental and accidental side effects occurred and must be considered.

There are some 200,000 living species in the United States, and experts believe that most of them are beneficial to man. The thousands of pesticides are registered for use against about 2,000 pests. Thus there are about a hundred nontargets for each legitimate target. Opinion is increasing that pesticides must be designed to be very selective in their killing power, rather than "shotgun" in their approach. Already too many "nontarget" species have been harmed.

Certainly we should be concerned about the dangers that pesticides present to man and his environment. Most people *are* concerned—including the relevant governmental agencies —and much research has been done and will continue. Environmentalists charge that pesticides are upsetting the natural balance, that some species are being wiped out, that pesticides induce cancer, and so on. Few of these claims have yet been borne out by scientific research, however. There is no proof that pesticides cause cancer or genetic changes in man, or harm unborn babies. Pesticides do kill through accident and through intentional use in suicides and homicides, however.

The government is aware that some sixty species are endangered, and that in the last few centuries many others have disappeared. Most of this extinction occurred before the introduction of the persistent hydrocarbons, however; in fact, of the sixty presently endangered species, only three are considered by the U. S. Department of Agriculture to be endangered by DDT and similar compounds. The rest are perhaps naturally dwindling, or are being killed off by other human activities such as city-building, hunting, and so on. According to the Pesticide Commission, about ninety-nine percent of all species have become extinct since the appearance of the first organism on earth some billions of years ago. They have gradually been replaced by species better adapted to the continually-changing environment.

The Commission recommends a "vigorous specific program . . . to bring the hundred most serious insect pest species of the United States under optimal control." Such a project would require about eighty percent of the insecticides now in use and could improve "specific insecticides, biological control methods, or integrated control programs."

There are some species that *should* be endangered—the anopheles mosquito, for example, and the pests that cause typhus and yellow fever. These and other diseases have killed millions of humans in the past and continue to kill many today—far more than the few killed each year by pesticides. It has been suggested, not entirely tongue-in-cheek, that we must begin to weigh the value of the disappearing peregrine falcon against that of man, who is also an endangered species.

Crop dusting by airplanes is an efficient means of controlling pests. —JAMES TALLON

Investigation of a fish kill near Poplar Bluff, Missouri, disclosed pesticide barrels used to float a boat dock in Otter Creek.
—ENVIRONMENTAL PROTECTION AGENCY

DDT and Other Poisons

There are two broad categories of pesticides. We have mentioned the persistent type, such as DDT. Its value—as well as its danger—lies in the fact that it remains effective for long periods of time. Some pesticides are not persistent and quickly lose their toxic effect. To be effective, however, they are much more deadly while they do retain their strength. An example is parathion, much used in agriculture. This deadly material has resulted in the accidental deaths of many crop dusters, field workers, and others. People who ate food stored in containers that had once held parathion, or children who played with such containers, have also died as a result.

On the other hand, there has never been a documented case of a death from DDT except for workers who have spilled quantities of the chemical on themselves, or people who deliberately committed suicide with DDT. Such a suicide is difficult, for massive doses of DDT, such as a teaspoonful at a time, cause no ill effects.

Because DDT is persistent, it remains on plants, and in soil, water, and even human or animal tissues. Because it is organic, it is taken up in living tissue. This is why we now have the problem of DDT residues in many living creatures, including man.

Today DDT is found in many organisms far from the point of application. It is said that cannibals eating human flesh would ironically be contaminating themselves with DDT residues. Even mothers' milk contains appreciable amounts of DDT, surely a cause for serious concern. Yet here is where the problem of pesticides is so complicated. For the Commission report, citing some 5,000 references in scientific literature, makes this statement on the effects of

pesticides on man: " . . . It appears . . . that present levels
of exposure to DDT among the general population have not
produced any observable adverse effect in controlled studies
on volunteers. The same is true of aldrin-dieldrin . . . "

Critics of pesticides have made some charges that cannot
be substantiated, however. Dr. Paul Ehrlich, for example,
stated at a public hearing in the state of Washington that
since its introduction DDT has probably reduced the life
expectancy of children by fifteen years. Another witness
pointed out that this could hardly be so, since in India,
where far more DDT is used than in America, life expectancy
has *increased* by about twenty years since the introduction
of DDT, and DDT is credited as a major factor in such
an increase.

As a result of its extensive investigations, however, the
Commission in its 1969 report recommended the gradual
phasing out of DDT in most applications, reserving it for
use only where there seemed no effective substitute. The
most important such application apparently is in the anti-
malaria campaign conducted by the World Health Organization. WHO has stated repeatedly that there is now no
known effective substitute for DDT, and that if it is banned
malaria will in all probability result in the deaths of great
numbers of humans, particularly in the undeveloped areas
of the world.

In view of charges that not enough testing has been done
on DDT, it is interesting to note that billions of humans
have been exposed to DDT for twenty-five years. Surely
this is as widespread a test as has ever been conducted.

Interestingly too, DDT use is declining, except in fighting
malaria and other diseases. In its place are non-persistent,
but highly toxic substitutes, which must be used with far
more care than DDT.

The Careless Killers

Parathion sprayed in a cotton field caused the illness of twenty-three agricultural workers in Texas. A pesticide plant in New Jersey was responsible for the arsenic poisoning of three workmen trying to repair equipment in the plant. Seven children in Florida died from parathion poisoning— they were murdered with it!

As the Pesticide Commission points out, safety is a relative thing. We could ban all pesticides and save 200 or more lives a year, plus much suffering. But there are many parallels to the pesticide danger which go unchecked.

Consider the automobile. We are now killing not 200 people but close to 60,000 people a year with it, and injuring millions of others. Yet there is no concerted campaign to ban the automobile, and rightly so, for it is hard to believe that we could continue to live in the manner we have become accustomed to without the automobile.

We must learn to live with pesticides because we cannot live without them. Within that framework there is still much that can be done to cut the toll of deaths and sickness caused by pesticides. Carelessness and ignorance are responsible for most of these needless tragedies, and here we can save lives through education, common sense, and better regulations. The Food and Drug Administration constantly turns up unbelievable examples of carelessness, not only by shippers and professional pesticide users, but by homeowners as well.

Most of us customarily handle these deadly poisons (they are so-marked on the containers) as though they were so much air freshener or soap and water! Stop and think about this for a moment. When did you last carefully read the warnings and instructions on the pesticide cans under the kitchen sink? Their very presence in this accessible place is dangerous, for children can easily reach them and turn the contents on themselves and others. With pesticides potentially as dangerous as guns, it is surprising that more of us aren't killed each year. Actually, more people die from aspirin and antibiotics than from pesticide poisoning.

Industry and professional users of pesticides are not blameless by any means. Accidents that defy belief happen in the handling of pesticides. Many of these occur during the shipment of chemicals by boat, train, and truck. The following are only a few examples of colossal carelessness on the part of people who should know better and must be made to do better.

The Fresno children who were poisoned by an organic phosphate insecticide did not contact it through food or water, or by personally handling pesticides. Instead the poison had contaminated the new jeans they had bought! Research turned up the fact that the insecticide had accidentally come in contact with clothing during shipment. Although it would seem that shippers would know better without being told, the California Legislature wisely introduced a law to prohibit the transportation of dangerous chemicals in the same shipment with clothing or food.

Investigating the death of 180 dairy cattle from pesticide contamination, Food and Drug Administration officials found that their feed had been shipped by railroad car; the car had been used earlier to carry crude arsenic trioxide, and enough remained in the car to poison the feed. To prevent the still-deadly chemical from causing further harm, 250 tons of feed and grain were burned and the dead animals were destroyed. The shipper of the feed and the railroad were properly cited for irresponsible handling of cargo.

In another case, paint pigment containing lead was shipped by railroad car. Some of it spilled, and later when the car carried potatoes the poison was circulated through the cargo by ventilation fans! A truck hauling oatmeal cookies also carried a load of the pesticide guthion; not surprisingly, some of the pesticide leaked out of its containers and into the cookies. Other truck shipments have contaminated milk, cooking oil, candy, and bakery goods with pentachlorophenol and other dangerous chemicals. One costly example was that of fifty-five-gallon drums of toxic chemicals leaking and contaminating a load of sugar. The sugar had to be destroyed, and the truck required a new floor and walls because the chemical had also soaked into them.

Loading of pesticides in ship holds along with food has also resulted in large losses. In such a situation DDT contaminated 7,000 crates of melons, and cheese and beer shipments have also been similarly ruined. Such discoveries are a tribute to the FDA inspectors, since they prevent death or injury to human consumers. In an attempt to stop further contamination, the Department of Transportation has issued regulations restricting the mixing of pesticides with food shipments and animal feed. But careless mistakes continue.

Perhaps the worst case of food poisoning by pesticides occurred in 1967 in Saudi Arabia at Qatar, where nearly 2,000 persons were hospitalized and twenty-six actually died from eating bread made from flour contaminated by the pesticide endrin. But the endrin got into the flour in the hold of a ship in which *drums of endrin were stored over the flour!*

A source of contamination not often considered is the stacking of pesticides with food in the supermarket. Putting a spray can of pesticide in a cupboard along with food is potentially dangerous, as is spraying the stuff in the kitchen without properly protecting food. Again, we must remember that pesticides are poisons, and must be handled as such.

Another factor in the pesticide problem is the use of

more chemicals than are needed. The approach is under-standable in one sense. After all, if a little is good, why not use a lot and be really safe? As a result the environment is subjected to more contamination than is necessary. More DDT and other material gets into soil, water, and air—and our tissues—and stays there.

The building up of defenses by pests against pesticides is also a problem. Flies can breed hardier strains that resist the DDT that once effectively killed them. Thus, greater amounts of increasingly powerful chemicals must be used to eliminate pests, resulting in more killing of nontarget species.

Living With Pesticides

The Pesticide Commission of course did not confine itself to advocating care in the use of pesticides. Leading off the Report was a list of fourteen recommendations which, if followed, would do much to eliminate the dangers that pesticides represent to our environment. Some of the high-lights:

——Closer cooperation among the Departments of Health, Education, and Welfare, Agriculture, and Interior on pesticide problems.

——Elimination within two years of all uses of DDT and DDD in the United States excepting those uses essential to the preservation of human health or welfare.

——Restriction of certain persistent pesticides in the United States to specific uses which create no known hazard to human health or to the quality of the environment.

7

THE DIRTY ATOM

A radiology professor testified yesterday
that the infant mortality rate had increased
in an area surrounding a nuclear power
reactor near Morris, Illinois.

Associated Press, October 22, 1970

Experimenting with cathode rays in 1895, German scientist
Konrad Roentgen produced, quite by accident, invisible
radiations that were so mysterious he named them X rays.
The strange rays could penetrate many solid materials and
had a special ability to reveal the bones and even the internal organs of a living organism, and they were put to
good use in medicine almost immediately. Since that time
it would be impossible to count the lives saved by X rays.

Just a year after Roentgen stumbled onto X rays, French
scientist Henri Becquerel discovered the radioactivity of
uranium. Here was a naturally-occurring parallel to man-
made X rays, and in time the discovery led to the unleashing
of nuclear power.

But just as pesticides have harmful side-effects, so too

does Roentgen's marvelous radiation. By 1936 a memorial was unveiled in Hamburg, Germany as a tribute to radiologists of all nations who had given their lives trying to save others. They numbered 110, and since that time more martyrs have joined them. Marie and Pierre Curie, who received the Nobel Prize for their research with radium, warned of the terrible danger that could come from misuse of radioactivity by *"les grands criminels."* Tens of thousands have died from the application of radioactivity to war, and the atomic bomb remains a threat to the world. But other dangers face us from radioactivity, resulting from our own carelessness.

In addition to the many who have died of X-ray exposure, many industrial workers painting with radium on watch dials have suffered similar fates, dying or enduring the agonies of cancer. Becquerel, during his experiments with radium, found that the stuff burned his skin near the pocket in which he carried it. Similar burns were experienced by X-ray workers—burns that led to warts and running sores, and sometimes the loss of fingers and arms, and finally a slow death. For years uranium miners had suffered from a mysterious disease named *"Bergkrankheit,"* or mountain sickness. We know now that this was lung cancer brought on by atomic radiation.

There occur in nature a number of unstable "isotopes," or special arrangements of elements. Uranium, radium, polonium, and cesium are examples. Because they are not stable, they emit radiation, either as electromagnetic waves, as particles, or both. Gamma rays, part of the emission of radioactive materials, are similar to man-made X rays. Such energetic radiation is capable of disrupting the atomic structure of whatever it strikes. Because this radiation has the ability to knock electrons from atoms of target material it is called "ionizing" radiation. Where most destructive phenomena take place only at a mechanical or chemical level, radioactivity can cause atomic changes in nonliving or living material. These changes include the destruction of cells and the mutation or genetic change of cells. Cancer is an example, and mutations in offspring is another.

The first warning of the X ray's serious danger came when X-ray workers began losing hair. From similar ionizing effects, radiation sickness killed or injured thousands in Nagasaki and Hiroshima after atom bombs exploded there in World War II. Some 300 others suffered radiation sickness, one of them dying, in a bomb testing accident on the Marshall Islands of the South Pacific in 1954.

It must be remembered that radiation has *saved* perhaps hundreds of thousands of lives and that nuclear power is important to our society. As with most other things, however, there is waste generated, and waste is potentially dangerous. This is what the concern over radioactive pollution is all about.

Just as there is natural pollution by dirt, minerals, and organic materials, there is natural radioactivity, including that which harmed European miners for generations before they knew what was causing it. This naturally-produced radiation is called "background" radiation and it exists everywhere, although it is stronger in some locations. One such area is a beach north of Rio de Janeiro in Brazil. Here "monazite" sands contain large deposits of thorium and radium, resulting in a background radiation ten or more times higher than the average.

In addition to radioactive particles, gases are produced by decaying radioactive elements. Examples are radon gas from radium, and thoron from radioactive thorium. In Chapter 3 we noted that radon is one of the minor constituents of natural air. Radioactive carbon 14 is also naturally present in the environment.

Before 1945 the only potential source of danger from ionizing radiation was the X-ray machine in hospitals, and radioactive materials used in treating cancer. With the first atomic explosion, however, man introduced radiation into the atmosphere in quantities that far overshadowed the background radiation to which he had become accustomed.

Atomic Pollution

Since the United States exploded the first atomic bomb at White Sands, New Mexico in 1945, our country and several others have exploded many nuclear devices. For a decade, so much testing was done that it became evident that radio-activity levels in the atmosphere were climbing dangerously high. In 1957 an Atomic Energy Commission report suggested that ten megatons (million tons) of atmospheric bomb tests in a year would result in from 2,500 to 13,000 defective children annually. Scientist Linus Pauling estimated in 1958 that tests up to that time would cause genetic damage that would eventually result in about 140,000 deaths and 140,000 defective children.

In that same year, as a result of worldwide pressure against continued atmospheric testing of atomic bombs, both the United States and Russia voluntarily stopped air tests, promising to explode future nuclear devices underground or in space. In 1961 Russia violated this agreement, however, and exploded an estimated 110 megatons of atom bombs that year. This was believed to have added half again as much radioactivity to the atmosphere as all testing up to that point had produced. Since then, Red China has exploded several large atomic bombs in the atmosphere.

X rays are dangerous, but only while they are being generated; once the machine is turned off, so is the radiation.

This safeguard does not apply to atomic bombs and other radioactive devices, however. Waste material or "fallout" continues to emit harmful radiation. The danger is thus analogous to that of persistent pesticides, and is compounded by the length of time such radiation can persist.

Radioactivity of various elements is measured in "half-lives," the length of time required for radiation to diminish by half its strength. A rule of thumb states that radioactivity is dangerous for five half-life periods. Uranium has a half-life of four and a half billion years, about the age of the earth itself. (Thorium has a half-life of fourteen billion years!) Half the original uranium is thus still present in the earth and will require a fantastic time to decay. Here are the half-lives of some other radioactive elements:

Iodine 129	17,250,000 years
Plutonium 244	74,000 years
Radium 226	1,600 years
Carbon 14	6,000 years
Strontium 90	30 years
Cesium 137	30 years
Polonium 210	138 days
Strontium 89	52 days
Iodine 131	8 days
Thoron 220	54 seconds

Obviously thoron with its very short lifetime is not a long-range radiation threat to man. Even polonium fades away within a few years. However, the radioactive elements that persist for many years are a source of concern.

Studies indicate that about four in 1,000 cases of cancer are caused by natural radiation. It would seem then that increasing the amounts of radiation in the environment would increase the incidence of cancer. So there is serious concern over the fact that man has added to the amount of natural radioactivity in the environment with his nuclear devices. Cardon 14, for example, was measured ten percent higher in 1958 than it had been before the atom bomb. With a half-life of 6,000 years, any danger that this increase represents will be a long time fading away. And some scientists believe that there may be adverse genetic effects from carbon 14.

Of more concern are the amounts of strontium 90, cesium 137, and iodine 131—all increased by man's nuclear devices. Strontium 90 is believed by some scientists to cause cancer and leukemia. Cesium 137 is thought to affect the reproductive organs. And iodine 131 may harm the body's metabolism through the thyroid gland. At one time after atmospheric bomb tests, children in St. Louis, Missouri were exposed to nineteen times as much iodine 131 as total background radiation.

The dangers from radioactivity are still controversial. One atomic scientist, questioned on the danger of strontium 90, pointed out that we would have to eat a ton of wheat to build up enough strontium in our bodies to be in danger. However, a reporter pointed out that in ten years we *do* eat a ton of wheat! Milk, tea, water, air, vegetables and other foods add to this amount.

Governmental concern over the dangers of radioactivity is evident in its maintenance of ninety water sampling stations, 250 air-pollution sampling stations, and sixty milk sampling stations. Milk is a particularly potent source of strontium 90, and the Department of Agriculture, the Atomic Energy Commission, and the Public Health Service have jointly developed a sterilization plant for removing the element from milk.

It was noted in Chapter 6 that persistent pesticides are dangerous because they are concentrated as they move up through the "food chain" to man. This same danger exists with radioactivity. Scientists were surprised to find that

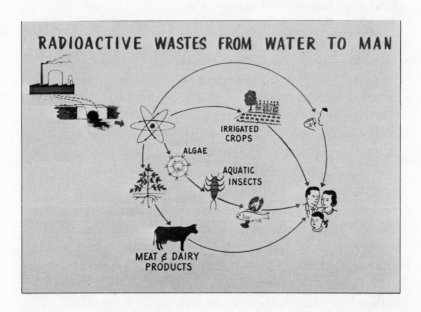

RADIOACTIVE WASTES FROM WATER TO MAN

IRRIGATED CROPS

ALGAE

AQUATIC INSECTS

MEAT & DAIRY PRODUCTS

Nuclear power causes severe pollution problems, although we cannot see, smell, or taste the pollution. —DEPARTMENT OF HEALTH, EDUCATION & WELFARE PUBLIC HEALTH SERVICE

Eskimos had acquired high concentrations of radioactive material in their bodies. Research finally showed that atmospheric radioactivity was taken up by lichen, which concentrated it; reindeer ate the contaminated lichen and further concentrated the radioactivity; and the Eskimos at the end of the food chain thus consumed radioactivity originally scattered over a huge area of the environment.

Dr. Sheldon Novick, a critic of atomic energy, has stated that fish have been found some distance from nuclear reactors with an 8,720-fold concentration of radioactive material in their tissues. And an incredible 350,000-fold concentration has been detected in caddis fly larvae in the Columbia River.

Radiation Hazard—Sooner or Later

How is it that something we can't see, hear, feel, or measure without special equipment is so feared by those concerned for man's well-being? In the days of Roentgen and the Curies, X stood for the mystery of this new and potentially lethal radiation. Over the years science has slowly and painfully learned what ionizing, or cell-killing, radiation does to living things. According to the Atomic Energy Commission the effects fall into two categories: acute (occurring within a few days) or chronic (occurring over a period of many months or years). Acute high-dose exposures either cause death within a few weeks or are followed by almost complete clinical recovery. Chronic exposures, if the dose is high, may produce gradually developing symptoms from which there is usually little recovery. A lower dose may increase the incidence of leukemia or contribute to other late, undesirable effects such as cancer. Radiation exposure may come from external sources or from radioactive materials that have moved into the body. External sources may produce either acute or chronic exposure; internal exposure almost always produces chronic symptoms. The immediate effects of radiation are bad enough, but the long-term hazards are of even more concern since they can affect the future of our race.

Continuing studies have been made of 700 radium-contaminated persons, the seventy percent alive of an original 1,000 known to have been contaminated, mostly in the 1920's and early 1930's, from radium and thorium. Uranium miners are also being studied. Long-range effects require some time to evaluate and there are as yet surprisingly few clearcut results from such studies. But there is an indication that cigarette smokers who are uranium miners are four times as likely to have lung cancer as smokers who are not miners.

In 1946 the Atomic Bomb Casualty Commission was

formed to undertake long-range studies of Hiroshima and Nagasaki victims. Only after twenty years did any effects other than leukemia begin to emerge in the 120,000 people under study. At that time, positive findings began to suggest a higher death rate than normal among the more heavily exposed, as well as an increase in tumors of the breast, lungs, thyroid, and stomach.

Among the victims of the 1954 Marshall Islands accident, thyroid gland abnormalities were found, and have been attributed to radioactive iodine fallout from the air. One case of thyroid cancer was found but not positively linked with the radiation exposure.

It is to be hoped that radioactive pollution from atom bombs will become less and less a danger. Although we presently carry in our bodies radioactive strontium and other elements acquired by breathing the air, drinking water and milk, and eating food, the levels are not considered dangerously high by health officials. If testing is eliminated, or is carried out underground or in outer space, the environment will slowly return to the background levels in which we developed and to which we have become accustomed. There still remains a potentially dangerous source of radioactive pollution, however. Unfortunately it is one that is increasing instead of diminishing with the years.

Go Play In the Nuclear Power Park

It is pollution from nuclear power plants that we must look at most carefully, for this may pose a far greater hazard to life and health than do the smoke, fumes, and other pollution now coming from our fossil-fuel power plants. In the early days of nuclear energy experiments, researchers learned how persistent are the pollutants from nuclear fuels or plants. White Oak Lake in Tennessee, built to receive radioactive wastes from reactors, demonstrated how living things could acquire buildups of residues far higher than those in the water. The nuclear plant, serene and smoke-free in a beautiful setting, may be a deadly menace to our well-being. The theory that what we don't see won't bother us is dangerous.

It is painfully obvious that peaceful uses of nuclear energy are flourishing and that even this prodigious growth is but a beginning. At present token amounts of electrical power are being produced by nuclear plants. In a decade the percentage will be appreciable; *in fifty years most of our power may come from nuclear plants*. What makes the problem so complex is that there is much argument in favor of nuclear power as opposed to the smoky, smelly, dirty power production by burning coal, oil and gas.

Advertisements by utility companies boast that a nuclear plant on the California coast is a good near-neighbor to President Nixon's California White House. Perhaps there is a nuclear plant near you, and likely it too is behaving itself. True, a nuclear power plant gushes no cloud of foul smoke into once-blue skies. There is no visible ash to shower down on irate residents miles away, no sulfur or nitrogen or carbon monoxide to kill vegetation, animals, and perhaps humans. All is nice and new and tidy and clean. And yet . . .

A nuclear power plant generates more waste heat than a fossil-fuel plant does, although it is expected that advanced nuclear reactors in the future will not do this. But reactors pollute the environment in more dangerous ways. First is the gaseous radiation that accompanies the production of electric power. Second is the waste left over after "burning" the fuel, somewhat analogous to the ashes left from coal or other fuel. Wastes from reactors and fuel fabrication plants are gaseous, liquid, and solid. Expended fuel packages are customarily shipped to a reprocessing plant, with some danger of contamination enroute.

Radioactive gases, completely invisible, pass out of the stack at the nuclear reactor and enter the atmosphere. These wastes continue to emit radiation, with half-lives measured in many, many years. As more reactors are built, more radiation will be added to the natural background.

Biologist Sheldon Novick states that about twenty years elapsed between the commencement of uranium mining and the use of proper safeguards for miners and the environment. It was reported that radiation in these mines was almost sixty times background. Novick notes too that twelve million tons of radioactive sand, refuse from uranium mining in the Colorado River Basin, were heaped in piles that could potentially affect seven states, and that wind and rain put radioactive wastes into air and water.

Because of the nature of the hazards of radioactivity, it is difficult to demonstrate positive proof of death or sickness caused by nuclear reactors. However, in 1970 a radiology professor from the University of Pittsburgh School of Medicine testified before the Pennsylvania Senate that the Dresden nuclear reactor, fifty miles from Chicago, had apparently increased the rate of infant mortality in the area since its installation in 1959. Dr. Ernest J. Sternglass claimed that studies made at the University indicated that infant mortality was linked to the amount of radioactive gas released from the nuclear plant. He also said that death rates from some respiratory diseases were correlated to the radioactive pollution. According to Sternglass, infant mortality increased about ten percent in Illinois, sixty-six percent of whose population lives within fifty miles of the Dresden reactor.

Sternglass' research involved normally operating reactors. Critics of radioactivity in the environment are also concerned with the possible results of catastrophic accidents at nuclear plants, or at nuclear waste storage sites. As part of planning, estimates have been made of life hazards at various sites in the event of nuclear blow-ups. One of these studies showed that personal damage might range from none injured or killed to an upper limit, in the worst case, of 3,400 killed and about 43,000 injured. Theoretical property damages ranged from a lower limit of about one half million dollars to an upper limit in the worst case of about seven billion dollars. It was estimated that people could be killed at distances up to fifteen miles, and injured at distances of about forty-five miles. Land contamination could extend for greater distances. This study was done in 1957, for reactors only a fraction the size of most now being planned.

There have been serious difficulties with nuclear reactors, although no catastrophes have yet occurred. But with larger plants, and more of them, there are increased probabilities of danger. Some nuclear reactors are built or planned in earthquake areas. Waste storage is accomplished on an interim basis in tanks buried underground. These might be subject to possible rupture from a variety of causes, with consequent pollution of the environment by products far more deadly than sulfur dioxide and fly ash. Concerning a reactor planned near California's San Andreas fault, one consulting firm estimated the effects of the release of only one percent of the radioactive fuel by earthquake:

In the event that winds on Bodega Head blew to the east and northeast, an unlikely but possible situation, the following exposures could occur. In the town of Bodega Bay, some two miles from the reactor, nearly everyone would die the first day. . .
One may conclude that people within five miles downwind of the reactor would probably be killed and within

The Connecticut Yankee Atomic Power Plant at Haddam Neck, Connecticut, produces 575,000 kilowatts of electricity.
—CONNECTICUT YANKEE ATOMIC POWER COMPANY

A nuclear reactor is basically a heat engine, its furnace providing heat to produce steam for a turbine which generates electricity.
—U. S. ATOMIC ENERGY COMMISSION

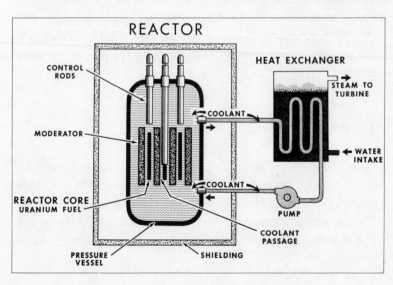

REACTOR

CONTROL RODS

HEAT EXCHANGER

STEAM TO TURBINE

COOLANT

MODERATOR

WATER INTAKE

COOLANT

REACTOR CORE
URANIUM FUEL

PUMP

COOLANT PASSAGE

PRESSURE VESSEL

SHIELDING

twenty miles many of the people exposed would be very sick. Beyond that distance a few would be sick within the first week and such long term effects as increased leukemia, thyroid cancer, and congenital malformations would eventually make their appearance. For distances of hundreds of miles from such a release of radioactivity the AEC (Atomic Energy Commission) . . . suggests, "Probable destruction of standing crops, restrictions in agriculture for the first year."

After an expenditure of several million dollars, the project was dropped.

Suggestions have been made that all reactors be built underground, that they be placed on the site of nuclear fuel and the wastes carefully put back where the fuel was taken out. In this way possible harm to the environment could be greatly lessened. It has also been suggested that nuclear power plants be built thirty miles offshore to reduce the hazard to human life.

There are many who argue that we should stop building nuclear reactors altogether—that society cannot coexist safely alongside such polluters of the environment. Strong disagreement to this belief comes, understandably, from those responsible for nuclear development. The AEC feels that nuclear power is not only safe but vitally necessary to the prosperous future of our country and the rest of the world as well.

The Atom Talks Back

Late in 1970 Dr. Glenn T. Seaborg, pioneer atomic scientist and former Chairman of the Atomic Energy Commission, strongly defended the AEC against the charges of its critics. Calling nuclear energy a "revolution that will prevail over the doomsday predictions," he said nuclear power would neither poison the air nor "boil off" the rivers. This has always been the stance of the AEC, as stated in its report "Nuclear Power and the Environment":

> The development of nuclear reactor technology in the United States has been characterized by an overriding concern for the health and safety of the public and for the protection of the environment. The safety record in comparison to other industrial activities has been excellent. No member of the general public has received a radiation exposure in excess of prescribed standards as the result of operation of any type of civilian nuclear power plant in the United States. As a matter of fact, no accidents of any type affecting the general public have occurred in any civilian nuclear power plant in the United States.

It is to be hoped that this view is correct, and that we really know the safe limits of nuclear power. It is true that in the AEC's experience since 1943 no member of the public has been killed or injured by radioactivity, although seven government workers have lost their lives in related accidents.

The radioactive carbon load of our air has been greatly increased since man began to explode or burn nuclear fuel, and there are also appreciable amounts of strontium 90, cesium 137, iodine 129 and 131, and other materials in the air, in water, and in milk. But the AEC believes that even concentration and reconcentration pose no harm for man. AEC human exposure limits are such that an individual who consumes about two quarts of water per day and inhales air at the concentration limit for his lifetime is not likely to be exposed in excess of the dose limits. Monitoring studies indicate that, in general, the annual radiation exposure contributed by nuclear power plants is comparable to the natural differences in radiation background commonly observed between geographic locations separated by several miles.

The AEC states that no adverse environmental effects

Radioactive wastes are sealed in ten-ton "vaults" prior to shipment to Oak Ridge National Laboratory in Tennessee for permanent burial.
—BROOKHAVEN NATIONAL LABORATORY

These fifty-gallon drums contain solid waste in the form of radioisotopes which emit alpha radiation. This dangerous form of waste is being buried at the National Reactor Testing Station in Idaho.
—NATIONAL REACTOR TESTING STATION

have been detected at its nuclear research sites at Hanford, Washington or the Savannah River in South Carolina, either from radioactivity or thermal pollution of streams. A Congressional committee in 1970 supported the AEC's position and voiced the opinion that nuclear plants are in many respects the least offensive power plants and can contribute materially to the fight for clean air. Also voicing a vote of confidence was Dr. Lee DuBridge, the President's science advisor, who felt that worries about radioactivity from atomic plants have been grossly exaggerated and that emissions from nuclear plants are far less dangerous than pollution from power plants that burn oil or gas or coal.

Along with its assurances of present safety, however, the AEC agrees that there are problems ahead: "The issues are not going to be resolved easily, and substantial understanding on the part of all parties will be essential. Provided that everyone seeks constructive solutions, there is indeed a basis for optimism that the many benefits of nuclear power can be realized without unduly affecting our environment."

Can We Live Without the Atom?

At the root of the problem is our increasing demand for more and more power for air conditioning, electric dishwashers, garbage disposals, waste compacters, toothbrushes, TV sets, and so on. While many people believe that warnings of the imminent exhaustion of coal and oil fuels have no validity, the trend is obviously toward more and more nuclear power. Today there are about a hundred reactors in this country. Some of these are fueled with as much as 350,000 pounds of radioactive material, fuel that will remain dangerous in some cases for thousands of years. Chances are that there will be no catastrophes. But this new radioactive pollution is far more serious than smoke and ash. If ten years from now we

Artist's conception of floating nuclear station producing power and water. The station would be moored offshore where it could obtain cold seawater at low cost and require no expensive land to isolate it from populated areas. It would produce 1,000 million gallons of distilled water per day and 3,000 megawatts of electrical energy, with these products carried ashore in conduits. —OAK RIDGE NATIONAL LABORATORY

discover that radioactivity in the atmosphere or our water or food *is* harming us genetically, it will do little good then to shut down nuclear reactors. The damage will be done and it will not be reversed. Nor will the environment become safe again for many years, considering the half-lives of many radioactive elements.

In 1950 each of us was using about 2,000 kilowatt-hours of electric power a year. This was equivalent to running a twenty-seven-horsepower engine for a hundred hours. By

1968 power consumption had increased to 6,500 kilowatt-hours a year per person. By 1980 it is anticipated that each of us will be using about 11,500 kilowatt-hours, and 25,000 kilowatt-hours by 2000. This will be about equal to running that engine 1,250 hours a year, or about three hours per day. And of course in 2000 there may be almost twice as many of us as there were in 1950!

Today only about one percent of all electricity is produced by nuclear reactors. By 2000 it is estimated that sixty-nine percent will be nuclear electricity. Thus, considering increased per capita consumption, radioactive pollution may be 250 times what it is now. With our power needs doubling every ten years, it is obvious that we will also be more than doubling our radioactive wastes, as nuclear power takes an ever larger share of the total.

By requiring less power—for example, by using less heat and cooling, washing dishes by hand, and using less lighting—we might put off the need for more power plants, but we probably won't. The building of more hydroelectric power plants is often suggested, since in these the "fuel" is free and no pollution is produced. However, the end of our water-power capacity is in sight, and hydroelectric plants will never be able to provide more than a tiny fraction of our needs.

The book *A Report on Fallout in Your Food*, by Roy Hoopes, ends with this warning: " . . . unfortunately the nature of the risk man faces with radiation is such that some men will live a little less long with it, and in not as good health, as some others. Anything that man can do to reduce that risk for himself and his descendants deserves serious consideration."

That care must be taken for the sake of our descendants is an important consideration. Failure to think of them will indeed make us the Curies' *grands criminels*.

8

NOISE POLLUTION: THE DECIBEL THREAT

The crescendo of noise—whether it comes from
truck or jackhammer, siren or airplane—
is more than an irritating nuisance.
It intrudes on privacy, shatters serenity and
can inflict pain. We dare not be complacent about
this ever mounting volume of noise. In the
years ahead, it can bring even more discomfort—
and worse—to the lives of people.

President Lyndon B. Johnson

The sense of sound is one of our most important means of knowing what is happening in our environment. We communicate with sounds; we are warned of danger by sounds—by a siren or a rattling snake, for example—and sounds serve to soothe and please us in music. We produce a waste product of sound too, in the form of noise. Noise has been accurately defined as unwanted sound. Unfortunately, but inevitably, unwanted sound is increasing and it may get much worse before it gets any better. In the meantime, noise is the one form of torture it is impossible to suffer in silence.

So serious is the problem that scientists for several years have been conducting experiments with humans and animals to study the effects of noise. What they have learned is not encouraging; much of it is alarming and even frightening.

Peace and quiet are two commodities that are becoming increasingly harder to find. Peace on a global scale has always eluded us, but in times past it has been possible for most individuals to find a retreat from the noisy workaday world. Today it is still possible but not very probable. Noise pollution—the crashing, squealing, shrilling, banging, hammering din of civilization—is no joke. It is a potential danger that should be ,carefully evaluated.

Automobiles, trucks, buses, motorcycles, aircraft, boats, factories, bands—all these noisemakers conspire against not only our eardrums but our minds and bodies as well. In their brainwashing techniques, the Communists have made clever use of noise to drive victims temporarily insane. To a lesser extent, but in similar fashion, the noises generated by technology do the same to us, sometimes without our being aware of what is causing our miseries.

There is a saying about it being so noisy a person "can't hear himself think." Physiologists, psychologists, and others concerned with noise believe that we *must* periodically hear ourselves think or suffer headaches, other bodily aches and pains, or even worse mental problems and disorders. The crash of garbage cans, the roar of buses, trucks, and airplanes, the din of a rock band, all can result in hearing loss for victims of noise pollution. Actually, deafness may be the least of the harm. Some concerned authorities see real physical danger from noise. Dr. Vern O. Knudsen, Chancellor Emeritus of the University of California at Los Angeles and an acoustical physicist, says, "Noise, like smog, is a slow agent of death." In his view, if noise continues to increase at present rates, it could become lethal for some human beings.

While not everyone—particularly those who are responsible
for noise—agrees with Dr. Knudsen's alarming prediction,
there is general agreement that noise is at least a major
irritant, contributing more tension in a society already beset
with stress enough.

It has been estimated that noise in the United States is
now about twice as loud as it was fifteen years ago. Again the
problem is twofold. There are more people making noise, of
course, but not enough of them to double it in that length of
time. Much of the added noise is caused by louder equipment
—power hammers, sirens, vehicles, and jets and other aircraft. An especially worrisome noise threat just over the
horizon has been the SST, the supersonic transport airplane
capable of flying faster than sound and in so doing producing
a "carpet" of deafening sonic booms below it. However,
the SST project has been abandoned, at least temporarily,
in our country.

What Makes Noise?

There are some basic facts about sound that we should be
familiar with in order to consider the noise problem in the
proper framework. Sound is created by pressure waves in the
air. Sound waves are longitudinal waves, actually areas of
compression and expansion moving outward from the source
of sound. These changes in pressure strike our sensitive (and
delicate) eardrums and are converted to signals which our
brain interprets as what we call sounds.

There are two fundamental characteristics of sound. A
sound has "frequency," the rate at which its waves reach our
ears. If thousands of waves reach us each second we call the
sound high-pitched, or high-frequency. If there are only tens
of hundreds a second it is low-pitched or low-frequency

sound. Frequency does not tell us the power or "intensity" of a sound. A high-frequency sound is not necessarily loud; in fact, it may be quite soft. And low-frequency sound can be very loud. The intensity of a sound wave is defined by a scale measured in "decibels," or tenths of "bels," the unit of sound strength named in recognition of Alexander Graham Bell. The decibel scale is logarithmic, and a sound with a strength of 80 decibels is not four times as loud as a 20-decibel sound, but one million times as loud.

The logarithmic scale is used for the convenience of engineers because sounds have such a great range of intensity. Our ears have a remarkable hearing scope, from hearing a pin drop some distance away, to being able to withstand (although sometimes with serious effects) loud noises nearby. There is a "threshold of hearing" below which we hear nothing, and another level above which our ears can respond no further. This range extends from zero to more than 140 decibels; we can hear sounds a billion billion times as loud as the softest sound we can hear. A rating of 140 decibels is the "threshhold of pain."

Just as we have decibel threshholds, there is also a frequency range for audible sounds. For humans, audible sound begins at about thirty cycles per second, a very low-frequency sound, and extends to 10,000 cycles for adults, and much higher for children. Many animals hear much higher pitched sounds. For example, bats "navigate" by a kind of natural sonar system that sends out and receives 100,000-cycle sounds.

It seems contradictory to speak of sound we can't hear, and unnecessary to refer to "audible" sound. If we can't hear it, how can it be sound? The situation is much like that of electromagnetic radiation. We see "visible light," from just above the infrared to just below the ultraviolet, but there is a much broader total spectrum of radiation than this. In fact, we see only about one-eightieth of the total electromagnetic radiation. Similarly, we can hear just part of the vibrations in the air or other media.

Just because we don't consciously hear sound does not mean that it has no physiological effect on us. Our brains seem to react to "subliminal," or below-the-level-of-perception, visual signals, and the rest of our bodies may be affected by radiation we cannot see. Ultrasonic (above the range of hearing) and infrasonic (below the range of hearing) sounds likewise have physiological effects on us.

The Sounds of Yesteryear

Noise is not a new problem. Man has been startled to the point of terror by the roar of a wild beast as long as both have been on the earth. And man has used noise to frighten his enemies in battle and the animals he has domesticated. Complaints about noise are probably as old as organized society. A report presented at a Congressional hearing on noise pollution pointed out that because citizens complained so much about the noise, Julius Caesar banned chariot traffic in Rome at night! And during the sixteenth century, laws were passed that prohibited Englishmen from beating their wives after ten P.M.—because the noise was a nuisance to the neighbors.

Charles Babbage, the nineteenth-century English inventor who has been called the father of the computer, claimed that noise in the streets of London destroyed one-fourth of his working power. Babbage saw a connection between health and noise levels; he pointed out that on his street of fifty-six houses there was always an average of twenty-six people ill, exposed to the "organ-grinders and other din."

Some people have lived with noise near waterfalls and rushing rivers. Most have been exposed from time to time

Representative Noise Levels

Object and distance from ear	Decibels
	140 (threshold of pain)
hydraulic press (3')	130
large pneumatic riveter (4')	
boiler shop (maximum level)	
pneumatic chipper (5')	120
overhead jet aircraft-4 engine (500')	
jet engine test control room	
unmuffled motorcycle	
construction noise (compressors and hammers) (10')	110
chipping hammer (3')	
woodworking shop	
annealing furnace (4')	
loud power mower	
rock and roll band	100
subway train (20')	
heavy trucks (20')	
train whistles (500')	
food blender	90
10-hp outboard (50')	
inside sedan in city traffic	
heavy traffic (25' to 50')	
small trucks accelerating (30')	
office with tabulating machines	80
light trucks in city (20')	
autos (20')	
dishwashers	70
average traffic (100')	
accounting office.	
conversational speech (3')	60
private business office	50
light traffic (100')	
average residence	
	40
	30
broadcasting studio	
	20
	10
	0

to thunderstorms and the noise of wind and rain. But over the years the sound and the fury of man-made noise has increased so that this natural "background" is hardly a factor any more. It is almost as though noise is the hearing tax we pay for progress in technology. Now, however, there are increasing protests that our technology should serve us better than this. Science and engineering that can give us a machine age including aircraft and other transportation should also be able to keep these things quiet enough not to threaten our sanity if not our existence. For there is increasing evidence that noise does endanger our health and perhaps our lives as well.

Industrial noise has been with us almost as long as industry. Hammers, saws, explosives, and a variety of other equipment produce waste noise along with their beneficial goods and services. Rivet guns and the clang of boiler factory sledge hammers have doubtless impaired the hearing of many workers. Through acoustical technology and a more humane attitude on the part of industry, protective devices are now available—and in many cases mandatory—for workers in high-noise environments. We are familiar with the "ear muffs" that aircraft technicians wear while working around jet planes at the airport. The shooters at marksmanship contests guard their precious hearing with scientifically designed and very effective ear protection. Even harassed citizens have taken to ear muffs or plugs to escape from noise.

The variety of noise sources is about as broad as the intensity and frequency spectrums themselves, but noise can be separated into a few general areas. The following examples are taken from hearings before the U.S. Senate Subcommittee on Air and Water Pollution in 1970:

OCCUPATIONAL NOISE Factory workers who are exposed con-

The unwanted sounds of modern technology give us noise pollution. And the noise gets louder and louder. —UPI PHOTO

Model of the Concorde SST being built jointly by England and France. It flies at about 1,300 miles an hour and creates a sonic boom some authorities feel will make it hazardous. —BRITISH AIRCRAFT CORPORATION

Map of estimated SST sonic boom "bang zones." —CITIZENS LEAGUE AGAINST THE SONIC BOOM

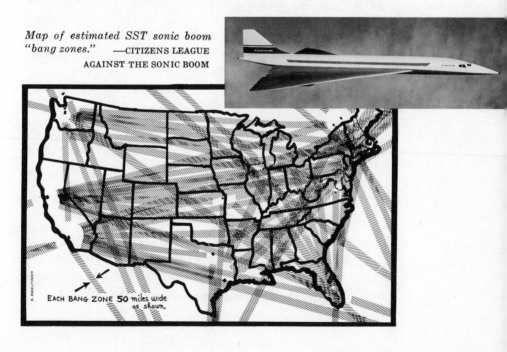

EACH BANG ZONE 50 miles wide as shown

tinually to high noise levels have poorer hearing than other population groups. An undeniable health hazard exists in this area, with as many as sixteen million workers exposed to such conditions.

AIRCRAFT NOISE In areas near airports or on airways, the noise of aircraft taking off, landing, or performing maneuvers . . . causes the greatest complaints . . .

TRAFFIC NOISE Away from aircraft noise, traffic is ranked as the greatest polluter of the quiet environment. The noises of trucks and motorcycles, which rise above the background roar of other vehicles, is especially condemned by those complaining of traffic noises.

OUTDOOR NOISE For those in the city, the noise of construction, emergency vehicles, and so on, are the greatest irritants. In the suburbs barking dogs, playing children, and lawnmowers cause the problem.

INDOOR NOISE Even man's home, long considered his castle, has been invaded by noise. Particularly in apartment buildings indoor noise is a problem, for here what is important or pleasant to one man may be noise heard through the wall or down the hall by helpless neighbors. Radios, phonographs, and TV all contribute, as do singing and the playing of instruments. The sounds of plumbing, furnaces, and air-conditioning, all become noise to some people.

SST: The Jet Bomber

One of the most controversial noises of our time is the sonic boom. Introduced explosively to the public when aircraft first broke the sound barrier, the sonic boom is perhaps the most sophisticated of man-made noises. Aircraft have always been rather noisy but most of the noise from subsonic planes is caused by the engines of such craft. The sonic boom, however, is caused by a shock wave created because air just can't get out of the supersonic plane's way fast enough. When flying faster than sound an airplane produces a cone of shock waves, and where this cone strikes the ground it produces the loud noise or noises (there may be a double or even a triple boom) we are becoming increasingly familiar with.

For a long time only military aircraft were capable of supersonic flight. So destructive have been the booms from these that homeowners and others have sued the government for millions of dollars in damages. The supersonic transport, or SST, is much heavier than military craft and thus creates a larger and more destructive boom. For that reason there is concerted effort on the part of many to "ban the boomers" by instituting legislation refusing permission for SST flights over populated areas.

Russia, France and England are already testing SSTs, and the Boeing SST was being developed in the United States. But critics claim that such craft would produce a devastating "carpet" of shock waves some fifty miles wide and the length of its flight. One writer claims that a fleet of SSTs would cause $24 million in damages *every day*, or a total of $9 billion yearly! Dangers he lists include the harmful startling of surgeons performing operations, painters on ladders, musical conductors, women in childbirth, and the ill and mentally disturbed.

Proponents of the SST claim that such tragedies would not occur and that supersonic flights over populated areas would not be permitted unless they were safe for all concerned. Special take-off and landing maneuvers are claimed to minimize the effect's of sonic booms.

The Effects of Noise

Not all sound is noise, of course; and a certain amount of noise even seems beneficial in some cases. It is well-known that children, and some animals, are comforted and sleep better with a loudly ticking clock nearby. "Sensory deprivation" studies in soundproof chambers have indicated that subjects become apprehensive or even disoriented in the complete absence of sound. Music is well-known for its therapeutic effect. It is used in many situations to provide a tranquil environment for workers, patients in hospitals or rest homes, travelers, shoppers, and so on. (Music can also have just the opposite effect. Much of today's music is actually considered harmful; certainly many are not soothed by a rock band playing in the middle of the night with amplifiers turned up to top level.) The sound of children playing, although it may be noise to some people, is generally a tonic. Laughter usually has the same effect.

The reaction to noise is subjective. The model airplane enthusiast with his shrieking gas engine is happy with the sound; helpless neighbors may consider it noise of the worst sort. Riveting or other industrial activity may be music to the ears of a factory superintendent with production quotas to meet, but agony for the residents in the vicinity. The whine of his lawnmower seldom bothers the yard man but it may aggravate a neighbor trying to sleep.

There are ways of reducing the harmful effects of noise. Many people play music or turn on a fan or other steady noise-producing equipment to drown out irritating noise. Ear plugs are used not only by industrial workers but by some sleepers. Acoustical insulation in walls and ceilings and on floors helps make noise more tolerable.

Some people seem more "allergic" to sound than others; some are seemingly unaffected by the most cacophonic noise.

But it is often impossible to determine the real effects. Some people endure noise at a terrible price to their systems, breeding ulcers, heart trouble, and even mental problems by suffering in silence. Quiet, at least at intervals, seems to be needed much as sleep is, to replenish our inner calm. As poet R. B. W. Noel put it:

> After battle sleep is best
> After noise, tranquillity.

Those noises most dangerous to our hearing are, understandably, loud noises. High-pitched sounds, particularly those that are pure in tone and long-lasting, make the danger even worse. The noise levels to which many of us are exposed incidentally are higher than those classed as injurious and requiring ear protection in industry. Rock music, for example, is often amplified louder than 100 decibels. There are now some sixteen million Americans—about eight percent of the population—who suffer some degree of hearing loss caused by noise of various kinds.

Hearing loss is only part of the noise problem, perhaps the least dangerous. A deaf man is not a dead man by any means; perhaps deafness is nature's way of protecting us from noise, as one cynic put it. Sound can and does harm much more of the human system than just our ears.

Noise affects the heart and blood vessels. It raises blood pressure and also the level of cholesterol in the blood. Noise can constrict small blood vessels and slow down the flow of blood. It can make the pupils of the eyes dilate, causing eyestrain and headache. Infrasound, in addition to hampering the breathing through pressure on the chest, is thought to alter the natural rhythm of brain waves. This latter result has been noted during the operation of "acoustical lasers."

Even while we sleep noises affect us in these ways and probably in other ways as yet undiscovered. Unborn children are affected by noise. Experiments show that noises can increase the rate of heartbeat in the fetus, and make it move and kick. Other experiments suggest that noises produce stresses that could induce developmental abnormalities.

There are still some people who live in very quiet environments. The Mabaan people of the African Sudan are in this category, and researchers have found that instead of being harmed by loud noises, or suffering lasting effects, the Mabaan recover very quickly from the shock of a loud noise. Also, they never suffer from high blood pressure or coronary disease unless they move from their traditional quiet home region into the city of Khartoum.

Such examples suggest that the healthier an organism, the better it resists injury from any cause, including noise. But our society has millions with heart disease, high blood pressure, and emotional illness, making us very susceptible to noise damage.

The noise threat is not a problem solely in the United States but one that other developed countries worry about too. Dr. Gerd Jansen of Ruhr University, West Germany, said before the Conference on Noise as a Public Health Hazard in June of 1968: "As several investigations have demonstrated, sounds or noises do change the physiological state . . . . Until someone proves that these physiological changes are negligible, we must consider noise to have a possible detrimental influence on human health."

Studies with animals suggest that perhaps far more insidious reactions are taking place as we continue to saturate ourselves in a sea of noises. Experiments with rats, for example, show that while they hardly seem to notice a 150-cycle sound at an intensity of 100 decibels (about the noise of a subway train twenty feet away), the rats undergo some remarkable physiological changes. The rats' pituitary glands release oxytocin, a hormone which in turn stimulates the excretion of salt and water from the kidneys. Oxytocin also functions to expel milk from the mammary glands during the nursing of young.

At the low end of the noise scale, a 20-kilocycle sound (a sound humans cannot hear) causes rats to freeze in what psychologists call the "alert position." At the same time the adrenal glands are stimulated and they in turn stimulate action of the kidneys. In other noise experiments, young mice were exposed to the sound of an electric bell at an intensity of 103 decibels for thirty seconds. As with the subway sound, there were no outwardly observable reactions. Yet when the sound was repeated a few days later, some mice suffered convulsions ending in death! Scientists call this phenomenon "priming" and find that it is highly reproducible. It works at a certain age level in the animals and apparently lowers their natural threshhold to seizures.

There is also a reaction to sound called the "startle response." Nature has taught us to take heed of loud or sharp noises. It would seem that all the noise we are subjected to would make us very tolerant and perhaps even immune to warning sounds. In fact, William Dean Howells made an epigram of this notion: "He who sleeps in continual noise is wakened by silence." However, the reverse has been found to be true. Researchers have learned that in a very high-level noise environment, consisting of traffic sirens, industrial noise, loud TV, radio, and record players, just one extra startle sound can trigger a violent reaction.

So noise is not merely a nuisance that from time to time threatens to drive us out of our minds. There is a much more insidious danger, succinctly expressed by Dr. Samuel Rosen, an ear specialist and medical researcher: "Adrenalin is shot into the blood stream. Heart rate increases, blood vessels constrict. There are reactions in the intestines. The acute symptoms persist. Actually they outlast the noise. You may forgive the noise, but your body never will."

Ear to the Future

There are two ways to lessen the harm caused by noise. One is to reduce the amount of noise; the other is to protect ourselves against what noise we can't eliminate. Both approaches have been used but much more can be done on both fronts. Counter measures will continue to be developed and applied only in proportion to the complaints of the victims.

Industry has taken some steps to quiet things down, and there are acoustical techniques and devices that result in less noise from equipment. There are even experimental techniques in which noise is defeated by creating another sound of proper frequency and phase to actually cancel it out.

Plastic garbage cans have been manufactured. There are quieter airhammers and drills. Silencers can be fitted on many noise-making devices; mufflers cut down on vehicular noise. Insulation and better design of buildings can help.

In England, the Noise Abatement Society secured passage of the Noise Abatement Act in 1960. Anti-noise groups are active in the United States, principally Citizens for a Quieter City, in New York; the National Council on Noise Abatement, in Washington D.C.; and the more specialized Citizens League Against the Sonic Boom, in Cambridge, Massachusetts. There is even an International Association Against Noise, which coordinates the efforts of groups in various countries. There are laws regulating noise, and a growing number of anti-noise cases are being heard in court. We cannot return to the "good old days" of peace and quiet. But we can *reduce* noise—if we shout loud enough about it.

9

A NATION GETS THE WORD

*. . . whatever the public chooses to have in the
way of environmental quality, it will have.
When these choices are made, it will
then become the responsibility of industry to
aid in the development and use of the
required environmental quality techniques. . . .*

K. R. Fitzsimmons
Shell Chemical Company

Pollution has at last become a dirty word for most of us, a
blight worth fighting against. Although there has been some
degree of protest for years from a few dedicated individuals
and groups, only recently has the problem become obvious
enough to enlist large numbers of people in more efforts. It
was inevitable that such an awakening would come; it is
unfortunate that it did not come sooner. As bad as the
various kinds of pollution are, however, there is still time to
reduce their causes and begin the difficult task of cleaning up
our dirty environment.

We are *all* polluters, and until we not only demand that

action be taken, but take action ourselves, the problems will not be solved. True, there are a few "bad guys," individual and corporate, who consciously and selfishly harm the environment, or at least don't help to clean it up. But the bulk of pollution comes from a whole nation of automobile drivers, trash burners, litterbugs, noise-makers, and patronizers of those industries that pollute in the process of satisfying our demands.

Wise men have always known the importance of a clean place to live. Hippocrates, more than 2,000 years ago, wrote that man's well-being was vitally influenced by "air, water, and places." A century ago, German biologist Ernest Haeckel coined the name "oecology" from the Greek "oikos" meaning home. In time the first "o" was dropped, leaving the simpler term "ecology" that is so prominent in the news today.

The Earth is our home; it always has been, and it will continue to be in the foreseeable future. Thus our environmental present and future depend in large measure on what kind of housekeepers we are—on how well we take care of our earthly home and how efficiently we use the natural resources which are our priceless heritage.

Several factors have caused the growing concern over pollution, and have brought about the beginning of action to clean up the mess. For one thing, the population of polluters is increasing at an alarming pace. World population is growing at its fastest rate in history, almost two percent a year. While this increase does not sound disastrous and may not even cause much concern at first, a closer look is very revealing. At two percent a year it will take only about thirty-five years to double world population. And each doubling starts with a bigger base. There was a time when twice the population meant "only" another billion. Then it jumped to two more billion. The next doubling will add almost four billion, and from then on the outlook is even gloomier. Coupled with the population explosion is the increasing use of fuel-burning engines to provide our many power wants. The atomic age and the space age have also compounded the problems of pollution.

Today there are young people who have never seen truly clear skies, or water unspoiled by pollution. The tragedy is that they are not even aware of this loss. Old-timers *can* compare the environment now with what it was in the past. Even making great allowance for exaggeration and lapse of memory, it is evident that air and water pollution are getting worse, and that solid waste and noise also endanger our environment. Quite suddenly the people in smoggy streets, along dirty waterways, and caught between deafening noise and the threatened horrors of radioactivity, have begun to demand that something be done—and soon.

The attack on pollution is fourfold, coming from concerned victims of pollution; from the legal profession; from the government (federal, state, and local); and from industry itself.

People Versus Pollution

In the last few years the Sierra Club and the National Audubon Society have doubled their memberships. To these groups, and to other traditional foes of environmental desecration including the Izaak Walton League, are now added such organizations as the Environmental Defense Fund, FOE (Friends of Earth), GOO (Get Oil Out), Ecology Action, Students for Environmental Controls, The Effluent Society, Environmental Action, and dozens of others. Millions of people, most of them young, participated in 1970 Earth Day "Teach-Ins" and other activities; some 2,000 college campuses, 2,000 communities, and 10,000 high schools took part.

All was not to the good, nor could it be expected to be. For example, the press reported that at one gathering eighteen tons of litter were left behind—nine times the amount expected from similar affairs at that location. Participants were urged to violence at some meetings. And some participants forgot their dedication when they learned that pollution could not be stopped simply by good intentions, placard-carrying, or placing all the blame on others.

But the stage is set, the climate and the temper of the country are right for progress. The extent to which people are concerned is evident in many places. A Houston television station requested comments on pollution, and 80,000 viewers responded—a fantastically high reaction. The people of Little Trenton, Maine, although in need of new industry and tax money, turned down a proposal for a nuclear power plant and an aluminum production plant in their area by a vote of 144 to 77.

In August of 1970, forty-three cars participated in the cross-country "Clean Air Car Race" from the Massachusetts Institute of Technology at Cambridge, to the California Institute of Technology at Pasadena. Engineering students from dozens of universities entered the cars, which included conventional gasoline engines, propane, natural gas, steam engines, turbines, electric motors, and hybrid types. Interestingly, even some of the gasoline engine cars met not only present pollution standards but those for 1980 as well! It was a conventional car that won the grand prize, in fact. Better maintenance of our vehicles would do much to reduce automotive pollution.

In 1970 the proposed regional jetport in the Florida Everglades was killed by The Audubon Society and other environmentalists who pointed out the harm it would do to the surrounding area. Windhoek, capital of South West Africa, became the first large city to directly recycle waste

Student projects can help fight pollution. This rubbish was collected from town streets in conjunction with Earth Day. —UPI PHOTO

One of the winners in the Clean Air Car Race of 1970, this entry used a conventional gasoline engine with smog reduction equipment added. —STANDARD OIL COMPANY OF CALIFORNIA

water for domestic purposes. And Suffolk County, on Long Island, banned the sale of *all* detergents. In all, it was a banner year—the year people declared war on pollution.

The New "Laws of Nature"

November 13, 1970, was an unlucky Friday for polluters. That was the opening day of a seminar on "environmental law" held at the University of Michigan and led by attorney Joseph Sax, long concerned with the legal aspects of pollution. A news release from Washington a few days later quoted the Justice Department as saying that for the first time in memory it was embroiled in a number of environmental lawsuits, "about thirty cases, some running into billions of dollars," involving the rights of the people versus developers of land and natural resources. These suits included a dispute over a Disneyland ski area planned for Mineral King, in the Sequoia National Forest in California, and a property rights battle between Alaskan Indians and developers of an oil pipeline in that state.

There have long been laws on the books against pollution, but unfortunately they have seldom been called into play. Today there is more concern about protecting citizens and the environment, and a number of legal groups have been formed with these interests in mind. In 1969 some sixty law students at Stanford University formed the Environmental Law Society. A sort of "environmental legal aid society," ELS quickly evolved into NELS, for National Environmental Law Society, with members not only at Stanford but Harvard, Yale, Columbia, George Washington University, the Universities of Pennsylvania, Virginia, Michigan, Chicago, Texas, Denver, Utah, Washington, and Oregon, Willamette University, Hastings, the University of

California at Berkeley, Davis, and Los Angeles, and the University of Southern California. Acting as an advisory service to all concerned parties, including legislators and individual citizens, NELS publishes a newsletter and the journal *Environmental Law Review.*

Some politicians in our history are remembered for their arrogant cry, "The public be damned!" Today the public seldom sits still for this sort of treatment by its servants. Politicians have learned quickly during the last few years that their constituents are interested in cleaning up the environment and are tired of waiting for the job to be done. So we have seen speedy, and in some cases effective, action on the part of public servants and those who are eager to move into such jobs.

America has had the Clean Rivers and Harbors Act since 1899. In 1924 the Oil Pollution Control Act was passed. In 1952 a Water Pollution Control Act Extension was passed and amendments passed in 1956. The Oil Pollution Control Act was brought up to date with new laws in 1961, and the Federal Water Pollution Control Act was passed. However, not until the Clean Water Act of 1965 was forceful action finally taken on the problem of dirty rivers and streams. At that time President Lyndon B. Johnson pledged himself and the administration to the task of cleaning up the Potomac River in Washington, along with other polluted waterways of America. In October of 1965 he said: "Clear fresh waters that were our national heritage have become dumping grounds for garbage and filth. No one has a right to use America's rivers and America's waterways, that belong to all the people, as a sewer." And most of the people agreed with him.

In 1965 a Clean Air Act proposed in 1963 by President John F. Kennedy was also passed, as well as a Solid Waste Act. And in 1970, as his first official act of the year, President Nixon signed into law the "National Environmental Policy

Act." At the New Year's Day signing, the President said: "The 1970's must be the years when America pays its debt to the past by reclaiming the purity of its air, its waters, and our living environment . . . It is literally now or never."

President Nixon also spoke of the environment in his February 10, 1970 message to Congress:

Because the many aspects of environmental quality are closely interwoven, to consider each in isolation would be unwise. Therefore, I am today outlining a comprehensive, thirty-seven-point program, embracing twenty-three major legislative proposals and fourteen new measures being taken by administrative action or executive order in five major categories: water-pollution control; air-pollution control; solid-waste management; parklands and public recreation; organizing for action. . . .

Of the thirty-seven points, fourteen dealt with water pollution, the problem that will be most costly to correct. Among other things, President Nixon's proposal asked Congress to:

_____Authorize $4 billion in federal money to match $6 billion in state and local funds for sewage-treatment plants in the next four years.

_____Encourage large-scale regional treatment facilities.

_____Allow fines up to $10,000 a day for water violations.

_____Authorize the Secretary of Interior to seek immediate injunctions where water pollution threatens health or irreversible injury to environment.

To move against air pollution, the following congressional measures were requested:

_____Tighter auto-exhaust standards, and regulation of gasoline and additives.

_____Research to produce a low-pollution auto, using unconventional power, in five years.

_____Fines up to $10,000 a day for violations of air quality and pollutant-emissions standards.

Federal law has required smog-control devices on all new cars since 1968. Emissions of carbon monoxide and hydrocarbons were regulated that year, and for 1970 stricter standards have been set. Also in 1970 trucks and buses for the first time came under federal regulation with respect to emission of pollutants. The Secretary of Health, Education, and Welfare has published more stringent standards for 1973, which will also include control of nitrogen oxides not now regulated. By 1975 particulate emissions too will be controlled.

The President introduced five proposals related to solid-waste control, including:

_____Research on techniques for reusing materials and producing packaging materials that will decompose easily after use.

_____Bounties for scrapping junked cars.

_____Incentives to speed trash disposal.

In November of 1970, President Nixon appointed William D. Ruckelshaus as administrator of the new Environmental Protection Agency. The new "environment czar" immediately informed the press: "We are going after all the polluters!"

The States Follow Suit

Not surprisingly, action by the federal government has been quickly echoed at the state level. Part of this response was undoubtedly caused by an eagerness to share in federal dollars allocated for pollution projects, but angry citizens provide another motivating force. Results are seen in recent state legislation, typical examples of which follow.

———Arizona, whose economy depends on copper production (it is the nation's leading producer), has drafted very stiff emission standards for smelters. And for a new coal-fired power plant at Page (near the Grand Canyon), the law requires the capture of 99.42 percent of fine ash particles from smokestacks.

———California, plagued most by automotive smog, has passed laws spelling out tight emission standards and imposing a $5,000 fine on car makers for each vehicle that fails to meet these standards in 1973. Similarly rigid water-pollution standards have been set for industry and municipalities, with $6,000-a-day fines for violations.

———Illinois has created an environmental protection board, with authority to control air, water, and noise pollution. Unprecedented powers allow this board to impound equipment, vehicles, vessels, or facilities for pollution violations. Even an airliner can be immediately grounded for smoking as it taxies along a runway at O'Hare International Airport.

Similar environmental protection boards have been set up in Delaware, Florida, Hawaii, Minnesota, New Jersey, New York, North Carolina, Vermont, and Washington.

———Maine, which stands to benefit by the establishment of Machiasport as a "free port" for oil, is attempting to levy a charge of a half-cent per barrel toward a $4 million protection fund against oil spills. Maine has also created a commission to monitor new industries to minimize harmful effects on natural resources.

———Michigan has revolutionized pollution law by permitting victims to sue polluters without first showing evidence of direct personal injury. The new law puts the burden of proof on the polluter, who must show that he is not creating a hazard. Already the Michigan law is being studied with interest by Colorado, Massachusetts, New York, Pennsylvania, Tennessee, Texas, and the U. S. Congress.

——The Vermont legislature aims to curb water pollution, which is the state's biggest environmental problem, by levying a "pollution fee" on all violators of regulations after July, 1971.

——And in Washington a special thirty-two-day session of the legislature on pollution resulted in "a whole string of bills" aimed at nuclear power plants, oil spills, and open-pit mines.

Local Pressure

Local governments, too, have applied pressure. Citizens of Greensboro, Georgia, fought and defeated a plan to establish a nuclear-waste disposal area on a 700-acre site because it would create pollution hazards. People in Calvert Cliffs, Maryland, blocked construction of an atomic-power facility for similar reasons. Home owners on Hilton Head Island near Beaufort, South Carolina, vetoed plans by a German chemical company to build a $100-million plant because it would result in air and water pollution.

The classic case of local conservationists versus power plants is that of the Storm King electric power generating plant near Cornwall, New York. Because of massive protests, developers agreed to install the facility underground so it would not mar the scenic areas. Citizens' groups at Escanaba, Michigan forced a paper manufacturer to build a cleaner facility and eliminate the "rotten egg" smell caused by the operation. In Detroit citizens have compelled authorities to file lawsuits against six major companies charged with pollution. In a similar action, 200 citizens of Fairport Harbor, Ohio, on the edge of Lake Erie, sued two industrial firms for $1.4 million in pollution damages. Funds for the suit were raised by many young people who went door-to-door and staged car washes.

Industrial Clean-up

Although industry is with some justice blamed for causing pollution, it is unfair to charge that industry has done nothing to fight pollution. Industry in 1969 alone spent about $1 billion on its own clean-up campaigns. And a poll of the 500 biggest U.S. industries showed that more than eighty percent of them believed in environmental protection even if it meant not introducing some new products, holding down production of existing products, or even reducing profit margins. Sixty-eight percent of these industries already had anti-pollution programs in operation. More than half felt that the government should increase its regulatory activities, and that there should be a single national standard for various types of pollution. Interesting.y, eight out of ten favored some kind of population control, although business has generally considered an increasing economy necessary to prosperity.

In 1970 industrial anti-pollution programs accelerated. One paper company announced a four-year, $101 million plan to equip its plants with primary and secondary water treatment facilities, and to upgrade its air-pollution equipment from ninety percent removal of pollutants to ninety-nine percent. Aluminum scrap campaigns were initiated, with the metal melted down and made into new material for industry. A California dairy inaugurated a re-cycling program, collecting plastic milk cartons for re-processing and sale as raw plastic to other industries.

New journals devoted to pollution problems are being published. Firms specializing in pollution abatement are flourishing, and the number of advertisements pointing proudly to what industry is doing is increasing. It seems that industry will do its part in the fight against pollution.

Let no one be fooled about the cost of cleaning up our environment. It will be high. Although it is not a well-known fact, we are already expending large sums of money. For example, we are spending $30 million a year just to *study* noise pollution. For all pollution the annual bill is about $10 billion.

This is a lot of money to spend and still get a dirtier environment each year, but $10 billion is only about one percent of our country's Gross National Product. Senator Edmund Muskie of Maine has asked that instead of $10 billion we spend $25 billion in the next four years to combat water pollution. Properly used, this would come close to bringing lakes and streams up to federal standards for quality by 1973, since the Federal Water Pollution Control Administration estimates that it will take from $26 to $29 billion to clean up our waterways.

To solve *all* our pollution woes, an estimated $100 billion to $120 billion will be required initially. Then about $20 billion yearly would be needed to keep the environment clean. Part of the problem may be voter acceptance; some Americans may balk at paying the high price and decide they would rather live in a dirty household. Yet, spread across the country and averaged out for our more than 200 million people, the yearly cost would be less than $100 each.

Some estimates for smog-free automobiles run as high as $300 in additional cost for control devices. But balanced against these costs are savings that may make a clean environment pay off financially in addition to providing a better quality of life. If pollution does cost each of us $65 annually—and many authorities say the true total is far more than this—then a family of four has a potential saving of $260 a year from a cleaner America.

The battle is not yet won, by any standards. Some cynics say we had better be thinking up a new name for ecology to keep public concern alive after that word is "talked to death." There are still some industrial polluters who refuse to cooperate. There are legal pitfalls, and the ponderous mountain of governmental bureaucracy may prove as difficult as a glacier to change in its course.

However, the 1970's began with wonderful promise in the battle against pollution. How well the momentum is sustained will depend on us—not just as citizens, students, workers, voters, and taxpayers, but as polluters as well. President Nixon cited a basic truth about pollution in his message to Congress on the environment:

> The fight against pollution is not a search for villains. For the most part, the damage done to our environment has not been the work of evil men, nor has it been the inevitable by-product of either advancing technology or of growing population. It results not so much from choices made, as from choices neglected; not from malign intention, but from failure to take into account the full consequences of our actions.

The next chapter describes constructive action that all of us can take against pollution, both in our own personal habits and in our campaign for effective government and industrial action. We can neglect the right choices no longer.

10

WHAT YOU CAN DO ABOUT POLLUTION

*Throughout history, all great movements
have started with a few individuals. And those
few individuals, at first, have always been
regarded as "nuts" or "fanatics" by society at large.*

Mercury Fleetfoot Service
Environmental Action, Inc.

Anti-pollution tactics must become a way of life for each of us, or at least for most of us. If we spurn smog control on our own cars, or disdain the use of biodegradable soaps and other products, all our shouting about pollution will only add to the noise-pollution problem. Happily there are many other things each of us can do at the personal level to fight pollution.

Don't be a power waster, for one thing. When President Johnson tried to inspire savings in electric power many jokes were made about turning off lights in the White House. It is true that one light can be burned for little money. But millions of lights burning needlessly, all requiring the combustion of a fuel that fouls the air, represent a great deal of *unnecessary* pollution. We also tend to leave the TV set or the radio on, or to heat our homes warmer than they really need be. Space heating uses about twenty-five percent of the fuel in our country. The English and many other foreigners use less heat and dress more warmly. We could follow suit. Refrigerated air-conditioning is a blessing in comfort but it consumes a great deal of power. Again we can save fuel and money, and produce less pollution, by letting our homes or buildings get a little warmer, and carefully monitoring to see that we are not using cooling power unnecessarily.

We probably will never go back to lighting our homes with candles or kerosene lamps, and a certain amount of electric power is needed for radio, television, and music systems. Home laundries are justifiable conveniences, for few of us want to scrub clothes by hand and few want to hang out the wash when a dryer is so much handier. But how vital are electric carving knives, tooth brushes, hair dryers, juicers, can openers, scissors, typewriters, swimming pool heaters, clocks, pencil sharpeners, and erasers? Instead of demanding, or meekly going along with, increased use of electric power, wouldn't it be a challenge to see how *little* we can get by on?

In response to pressures against water pollution, some manufacturers are producing phosphate-free soaps and detergents. Are these used in your home? If there is not broad public acceptance of products designed to be easier on our environment, the firms producing them will have no incentive to continue. Instead, they will be at a disadvantage in the market, since such products probably cost more to produce.

Open burning is a great contributor to smoky skies; do as little of this as possible. Many communities have outlawed the open burning of trash, but enforcement of such laws is difficult without the help of all. It is true that burning is often the cheapest and easiest way to get rid of wastes. But consider your downwind neighbor, and remember that much of the pollution you must endure came from someone who was inconsiderate of *your* environment. Use your fireplace less often. Do less backyard barbecuing. And use leaves and grass cuttings for compost instead of burning them.

Since our automobiles are to blame for about sixty percent of the total air pollution in America, the less we use them the fewer exhaust fumes we pump into the air. So walk on short trips, ride a bike or motorbike, rather than taking the car. Form car pools so that fewer gallons of gas are burned per passenger mile. By far the majority of autos on our streets carry one person when they are designed to hold six.

Check your car to see if it is smogging up the atmosphere. Some states have compulsory vehicle inspection which includes a check of the crankcase and exhaust for cleanliness. Many do not, however, and it is up to individual car owners to police these contributors to dirty air. Newer cars are equipped with smog-reducing equipment but there are many older models still on the road, some of which dump excessive amounts of pollutants into the air. Even new cars must have their smog-control devices properly maintained. While a functioning device greatly cuts the amount of pollutants escaping into the atmosphere, one that is improperly maintained may cause more pollution than an un-equipped engine. Some inconsiderate drivers disconnect smog devices, because they feel that this equipment reduces power and gas mileage. Obviously if many of us take this attitude, all the regulations and technological improvements men can devise will not do the job.

Water transportation is not as large a pollution factor as surface vehicles are, but even here you can take action. To reduce noise pollution, go sailing or rowing instead of using a motorboat. And don't dump garbage or other wastes into the water while you are boating.

There are many ways to help cut down noise pollution. Be considerate of others with TV, stereo, radio, musical instruments (particularly those with amplifiers!). You might even ask local stations to suggest that listeners turn down their radio and TV at about ten P.M. If garbage cans are a noise problem in your neighborhood, investigate the use of plastic cans. Or line the metal ones with burlap bags to deaden the sound. Check the muffler on your car or motorcycle. Don't use a power lawnmower if you have only a small yard to mow. If possible, clip the hedge and do lawn edging by hand instead of using noisy power tools.

Make another great personal contribution to a cleaner environment by cutting down on solid wastes. Packaging is one of the greatest factors in this kind of pollution; by carrying a shopping bag to the store, you can reduce the amounts of packaging necessary. Returnable bottles and other containers also save packaging; they may not be as convenient, but they will help clean up the environment and will also save you money. Someone has to pay for throw-away containers, and it is the customer who is at the end of the economic line.

It is estimated that the average family in our country spends about $24 a year on disposable cans and bottles for beverages. Packaging, including bags, wrapping paper, cellophane, plastics, tinfoil, waxed paper, styrofoam, and so on amounts to about $500 a year per family. So carry a lunch box instead of a paper sack. Use scrap paper for note pads, children's drawings, and so on. Save wrapping, particularly gift wrap, for reuse. Newspapers and other paper products are a large part of the solid waste problem. In some cities there are segregated waste containers for separation and re-cycling of paper wastes. Many groups collect waste paper and sell it for re-use. Check in your community for places to sell, or at least turn in, paper waste.

Volunteers bring in cans for combined clean-up drive and recycling effort. Campaigns like this one in Phoenix, Arizona, are being duplicated in many other cities.

—THE PHOENIX GAZETTE

This barrel of cans is being weighed so collectors of this solid waste can be paid. Aluminum is especially desirable for recycling.

—THE PHOENIX GAZETTE

A scarecrow of tin cans and other litter reminds motorists that "every litter bit hurts." The 4-H Club of Hardenville, Missouri, created this effective piece of modern sculpture as their contribution to clean living.

—UPI PHOTO

Know the Problem!

Perhaps by now you are beginning to question some of the suggestions on curbing pollution. This is a good sign because as we move from such obvious helps as not throwing banana peels on the sidewalk it becomes harder to make judgments. Which is worse, a garbage disposal unit, or a garbage can in the alley? In the long run, which pollutes more, a gasoline-fueled automobile, or an electric one recharged by electricity produced in a coal-fired power plant?

One weakness of both individual action and group efforts is ignorance of the facts. Unfortunately, many well-meaning people and organizations are half-informed and too hasty in their attempts to improve the situation. Even the best-intended persons make a poor impression on industrial leaders, government officials, legislators, and their fellow citizens when they obviously haven't thought out the problems and don't have a good grasp of what they are talking about. Demands to completely shut down a mine in the neighborhood, for example, would probably be met with hostility by those who depend on mining for a living. And frenzied pleas for a subway costing millions of dollars a mile wouldn't make much headway in an area where it will serve only a handful of people. The pollution problem is not nearly as simple as it sometimes appears. If we are to do something constructive about it we must understand the problems, the causes, the potential solutions, and the methods of putting these solutions into practice.

It is easy to say that we should stop using paper napkins, plates, and plastic knives, forks, and spoons. But when we substitute cloth napkins, china, and silverware, don't forget that these must be washed. In most cases, this uses quantities of water and electric power and pollutes our water with phosphates and other harmful chemicals. Nor can we forget that if no one uses paper napkins, the people making them are going to be out of work. Solutions that involve beating up mine owners and bombing chemical plants are not really solutions at all.

In the back of this book is a bibliography of literature on pollution. Your library will most likely list more material in the card catalogs and the *Readers Guide to Periodical Literature.* Some literature on the subject unfortunately has been written at white heat, and sheds little light on the real situation. Much has been written by apologists for polluters, for example, and much has been authored by opportunists who see the pollution crisis as a way to make a quick buck by joining the ranks as a militant anti-pollution fighter. The serious person must wade through these conflicting stories to find the truth; he must then make some decisions for himself.

Getting Involved

The pollution problem is not going to be solved overnight by our individual efforts, or even by the most concerted efforts at the government level. One Earth Day won't do the job. It will help little to make speeches and print anti-pollution leaflets if we then leave our soapboxes in the public square with thousands of leaflets blowing in the wind to add to the pollution problem.

Use some common sense. At one school on Earth Day, water, lights, and air conditioning were turned off to bring home the fact that they are needed. The tactics of some anti-pollution and environmental groups are questionable. It does no good to smash a new car to pieces with a sledge hammer or to bury cars. Most air pollution protesters arrive for their speeches in cars, buses, planes, and so on; few of them walk or ride bicycles.

A few activists advise taking a bottle to the grocery store and filling it with milk from a paper milk carton, or removing the cardboard packaging from products and handing them back to the clerk. Such action might serve as a dramatic message once or twice, but if continued it could lead to charges of nuisance or harassment. Those who make it a habit to dump empty cans on factory lawns would do better not to buy such products in the first place, or to suggest improved ways of packaging. The same goes for those who would ban all pesticides and preach the use of organic fertilizers, including human wastes. It is generally agreed by agricultural experts that we could not feed the world without pesticides and commercial fertilizers, and that disease can be transmitted by human wastes. But some pseudo-ecologists continue to suggest or even demand such ill-advised farming methods.

The height of irony is the anti-pollution meeting featuring *bumper stickers* urging us to "Ban the Automobile!" *metal* buttons proclaiming "Don't waste our Priceless Metals!" or *plastic* buttons that read "Use Biodegradable Products!" Stacks of paper plates, paper napkins, plastic cups, and throw-away beverage cans make such an affair ridiculous— except to point out how difficult the pollution problem is.

Once you do have a realistic understanding of the problems, you can begin to take effective action, either as a lone wolf or as part of a conservation or anti-pollution group. Such campaigns take various forms. Earth Day and similar informational demonstrations are examples. Education is vitally important, for unfortunately there are still many people who don't understand the problem or who don't even know there *is* a problem. Clean-up campaigns are good attention-getters; they tend to snowball and involve more people in the fight. You can clean up your neighborhood. In parks, fields, and along the highways, trash can be removed to make the environment more pleasant to live in and drive through. Talk to others and get them to help in anti-litter drives.

How does your school stack up in the fight against pollution? Do its incinerators foul the air? Is the campus littered, and if so whose fault is it? Are there pollution sources nearby that affect the campus environment—mines, mills, sawmills, chemical plants, open dumps, and so on? How many courses taught at your school relate to pollution and the environment? Have you discussed this with your science teachers, advisers, principal, school board? Is there a district or state plan to add such courses if they are not now offered?

You might want to consider a career in environmental science. Much importance is being given to such work, and at the University of California at Los Angeles a new Doctor of Environmental Science and Engineering degree is being offered, requiring five years of graduate work, including three years of classroom work and two in government or industry.

Art students can produce effective posters on pollution. Science classes can plan projects investigating pesticide contamination, water pollution, smog, and so on. Pollution is an excellent subject for book reports, speeches, and assembly programs. The topic for the "High School Debate, 1970-71," is "How Can Our Physical Environment Best Be Controlled and Developed?" Here is an opportunity for young people to make themselves heard in the cause for a cleaner environment. If there is an anti-pollution group at your school or in your community, join it. Often many can do more than an individual can, and a group tends to encourage its members and keep working far longer than one person could or would.

Form an ecology club, asking help from established and reputable organizations such as the Izaak Walton League, the Sierra Club, and others. Projects might include a field day to clean up a small lake shore. Some groups "adopt" a lake or river and work to make it better. Newspapers will generally publicize efforts of this sort.

One national group called SCOPE (Student Councils on Pollution and the Environment) has been established in nine regions corresponding to the Department of Interior's Federal Water Quality Administration areas, and members meet periodically with government officials. Former Secretary of the Interior Walter Hickel proposed a National Environment Control Organization for young people who want to take a full-time role in the fight for a better environment.

In California, Nevada, Idaho, and Hawaii, there is a program called "Community Pride," sponsored by Standard Oil Company of California and the 4-H organization. More than 8,000 young people from nine to nineteen years of age are involved in environmental conservation programs including clean-up campaigns and tree planting on burned-out or otherwise desecrated landscapes. The Boy Scouts of America too are deeply involved in the fight against pollution; their Project SOAR (Save Our American Resources) is aimed at air and water pollution abatement, litter prevention, waste disposal, and re-cycling.

You Too Can Be A Lobbyist

Even the most diligent and well-informed individuals or groups cannot do all the work by themselves, of course. There must be proper regulations, effective laws, and incentives. There must also be suitable penalties for those who refuse to comply with such rules and regulations, for there are people who will never do more than they are forced to do.

Government officials and legislators tend to be quite

responsive to their constituents, particularly during election years. Most of the new anti-pollution legislation mentioned in Chapter 9 was passed under pressure from concerned citizens. Legislative hearings are for the most part open to the public; lobbyists for industry and agriculture can attend them and effectively make their pleas. As a citizen affected by pollution, you have a right to be heard too, so don't miss out on this opportunity. It is a political fact of life that the squeakiest wheel gets the most grease, in this case in the form of corrective legislation.

Learn about the various agencies in your town, city, or state. See if you have an agency controlling air pollution, water pollution, pesticides, and noise. How about solid-waste control? Are there open, burning dumps in your area? Why not landfills? What kind of sewage plant do you have, or do homeowners have to provide septic tanks? How is your domestic water treated before you use it? *After* you use it? How is your electric power produced? Do the power plants pollute the air? The water? What becomes of ash and other solid wastes? What are the amounts of the various contaminants and how do these compare with pollution standards?

If it is obvious after careful study that more could be done to fight pollution, don't hesitate to take action toward doing so. In some communities there are groups already formed for this purpose, but elsewhere there is a need for more action. In Arizona's 1970 legislative session, for instance, a number of anti-pollution measures were introduced. Major legislation, clarifying air pollution laws and giving more control to state agencies, was passed. However, bills to encourage the use of returnable beverage containers, and to outlaw internal-combustion automobile engines by a certain time died quickly. The only hearing witnesses in both cases were those opposed to such legislation, and there were many. No concerned citizens urged that the bills be passed; few bothered even to write, phone, or visit their legislators. Such lack of action indicates to legislators that there is little public concern, and therefore little need for passage of such bills.

Letter writing is effective. Letters should be temperate but firm, pointing out the problem and the suggested solutions. Telephone calls should be in the same vein. Demonstrations should remain orderly and intelligent. Some legislators do not appreciate, or even permit, gas mask drills, the hanging of polluters in effigy, and the like.

There is an old saying that goes: "If *you* don't do it, it won't get done." This should be the motto of all of us who want to do something about pollution and are willing to put out the necessary effort. Again, don't expect miracles as soon as you start to fight pollution. But everyone can help. On the following pages are a pollution checklist, and the names and addresses of agencies, organizations, and publications that may be helpful in your campaign to clean up the environment. Good luck!

CHECK LIST FOR YOUR COMMUNITY
(From the journal *Pollution Engineering*)

1. Does your community have pollution control laws—air, water, noise, solid waste? Have these laws been revised in the past five years?
2. Do you have a copy of your community's pollution control laws?
3. Does your community have adequate personnel to test for pollution and enforce control laws? All day, every day?
4. Do you know how to report a pollution violation?
5. Do community schools conduct courses on environmental control? For adults also?

6. Is there a community conservation club?

7. Who do you think is creating pollution in your town? What kind of pollutants do they create? What are they doing to control it? Have you discussed pollution with them?

8. Does your community provide any tax incentives or relief measures for installation of pollution abatement systems?

9. What pollutants from sources outside of town blow or flow into your community?

10. Does your town test for pollution?

11. Does your community have a pollution emergency warning system?

12. How often must windowsills in your homes and schools be cleaned of air-borne dust?

13. How often are homes repainted in your town?

14. Must you wipe dirt and grease from clotheslines before hanging up wash?

15. Do you burn garbage, branches or leaves?

16. How does your community dispose of garbage?

17. Is refuse permitted to accumulate on streets and in vacant lots?

18. Are there adequate numbers of refuse containers on street corners and in parks?

19. Do people abandon cars on the streets of your town? Are there penalties for doing this?

20. Are gutter downspouts connected to a storm sewer?

21. Does flooding regularly occur after rainstorms?

22. Are there ever water shortages or restrictions in your community?

23. Would you swim in or drink water from rivers, lakes, and streams in your town?

24. Are beaches or picnic sites ever temporarily closed because of pollution?

25. Do fish live in streams flowing through your town? What kind—scavenger or game fish?
26. How often are streams and rivers in your town cleaned?
27. Are all homes connected to sewer systems?
28. What kind of sewage treatment does your town provide?
29. What type of materials do you put down the sewers— detergents, paint, cleaners, poisons, etc.?
30. What kind of water supply treatment does your community provide?
31. Does the sound volume from your television or radio annoy other people?
32. Do you have to raise your voice to be heard above the noise from appliances or machines?
33. Are you willing to spend some time and money by volunteering to help your community fight pollution?

FEDERAL AGENCIES

Environmental Protection Agency
1626 K St. N. W.
Washington, D. C. 20460

National Air Pollution Control Administration
Arlington, Virginia 22203

Federal Water Pollution Control Administration
U.S. Department of the Interior
633 Indiana Avenue, N.W.
Washington, D.C. 20240

Bureau of Solid Waste Management
Department of Health, Education, and Welfare
Washington, D.C. 20201

Office of Noise Abatement
Department of Transportation
Washington, D.C. 20553

Department of Agriculture
Washington, D.C. 20250

(Look up your state organizations in the telephone directory
or call the Governor's office for information.)

PRIVATE ORGANIZATIONS

The Izaak Walton League of America
1326 Waukegan Road
Glenview, Illinois 60025

National Audubon Society
1130 Fifth Avenue
New York, N.Y. 10028

The Sierra Club
1050 Mills Tower
San Francisco, California 94104

Citizens for Clean Air
40 W. 57th St.
New York, N.Y. 10019

Citizens for a Quieter City, Inc.
Box 777, FDR Station
New York, N.Y. 10022

HELPFUL PUBLICATIONS

Clean Water—It's Up to You Izaak Walton League	Free
Community Action For Environmental Quality Government Printing Office Washington, D.C. 20402	$ .60
Solid Waste Management National Association of Counties 1001 Connecticut Ave. N.W. Washington, D.C. 20036	Free
Workbook for Clean Air The Conservation Foundation 1250 Connecticut Ave. N.W. Washington, D.C. 20036	Free
Youth Takes the Lead Urban Research Corp. 5464 South Shore Drive Chicago, Illinois 60615	$1.95

11

A CLEANER WORLD TOMORROW?

*The time span remaining for constructive action
is short. The future slips into the past at a
blurred clip and our hope lies with those
whose vision is as wide as the problem
and whose courage is a match for the corrective
measures so urgently needed.*

"Man . . . An Endangered Species?"
U. S. Department of the Interior

Pollution, the fouling of our environment, is a disgustingly evident fact of life. When a river is so chemically polluted that it bursts into flames; when lakes are being hurried to an early death by oxygen deficiency, when marine industries dependent upon oysters and many kinds of fish have been destroyed; when the air is so dark with pollution that airplanes, and even surface traffic, are endangered and some city dwellers inhale the equivalent of two packs of cigarettes a day without even smoking; when garbage, trash, and other solid wastes pile in ever-mounting heaps of smoking, stinking refuse—then, we are in big trouble.

There is encouragement in the fact that man himself is responsible for most of the pollution. If instead there were meteorological causes only, or earthquakes, or naturally caused forest fires, or if animals were the major foulers of the earth, the problem might be beyond hope of correcting. But man is the guilty party, and what he has done by accident and incident for centuries he may in less time be able to minimize by intent and design. The situation is really simpler than that—we *must* minimize pollution or one day be literally choked and buried in our own waste.

Understanding is the key to solution, and there is evidence that some people do understand the problem and are working toward real solutions. Unfortunately, there are others who merely stand on the sidelines and complain or criticize. Some don't realize anything is wrong. Meanwhile, all of us are still contributing to the problem.

If we were suddenly able to eliminate all the brazen and inconsiderate polluters who do so to their own advantage, the major share of pollution would still remain. To review— we pollute with our mines and our power plants, our surface vehicles, ships, and aircraft, our laundry and our sewers, our agriculture, and our thousands of industries.

The question is no longer whether we have a problem, but what to do about it. First, can we hope to *eliminate* pollution? Dr. Lee DuBridge, President Nixon's former science advisor, had this to say:

> If the Government issued a law that no one could pollute the air or water, what would happen?
>
> Every automobile would be put in the garage to stay. Every bus and truck and airplane and diesel locomotive would be stowed away—inoperative. The entire transportation system of the country would come to a complete halt. Every power plant would be shut down. We'd have a permanent blackout.... Almost every industrial plant would have to be shut down.

There would be no way to bring food to market. There would be no power to propel the plows and agricultural machines that process, fertilize, and harvest our crops. Our population would be dead in a moderately short time—really dead. Our whole civilization would collapse.

All this, of course, is an exaggerated example. The point is that we have to find a place somewhere between today's level of pollution and that of long ago. We have to determine what are tolerable, reasonable levels of pollution consistent with good health, and then aim to hold pollution to those levels.

Most thoughtful people realize that we will never completely get rid of pollution and pollutants. The best solutions we can hope for will be compromises.

Ideally, we can put wastes to good use. The growing of fish or of plant crops in warmed or "thermally polluted" water is a classic example. The use of sewage sludge for fertilizer is another. The reclamation of many other wastes for re-cycling, including metals, chemicals, and paper can also be accomplished. Conservation of our resources, the using of a little rather than a lot, can go a long way toward easing the pollution problem, too. When it becomes fashionable to walk more instead of riding, to use less energy for heating and cooling, and to use our muscles for a number of tasks we now do with the flick of an electric switch, we shall also reduce pollution.

London: A Shining Example

Already significant achievements have been made. London is a shining example of what can be done. In this historically dirty city, where more people have died or been made ill from pollution than anywhere else, determined action has resulted in almost unbelievable improvement.

After centuries of choking fogs and soot-grimed buildings and lungs, London had finally had it by 1956. Hundreds of tons of soot settled on each square mile of the city every year and an estimated 30,000 Londoners died of bronchitis, with thirty-five million working days lost annually by living sufferers. In the killer smog of 1952 a duck crashed into the glass roof of Victoria Station and fell at the feet of passengers who were waiting until the trains could move again. Theatergoers could see plays or movies only if they were fortunate enough to get front-row seating. At a performance of *La Traviata*, singers were unable to see the conductor, and the curtain had to be rung down. Cattle brought into town for the Smithfield Show, an animal fair with prizes for the best stock, died in the unhealthy atmosphere. *And smog killed 4,000 people in London that terrible winter week.*

The Clean Air Act was passed in 1956, giving officials the authority to restrict domestic heating to smokeless fuels. Because eighty percent of London's air pollution came from house chimneys, this remedy worked, especially when fuel dealers were ordered to stop selling fuel that would smoke. To ease the financial strain, the government paid seventy percent of the cost of converting heating plants to electricity, oil, or other smokeless heat. And, remarkably, the Clean Air Act produced clean air.

Implementation of the Act was no easy thing, and there was grumbling and fighting about switching to more expensive ways of heating. But the anti-pollution forces slowly prevailed, and today it would be hard to find people who do not like what they have bought with their effort and money. Londoners are finding that in the long run instead of costing money, the cleanup has saved them money.

So effective was the Act that London has changed from a dingy, dirty, smoky place of sooty black buildings to a bright and cheerful city of blue skies. Hardly believing their eyes, scientists measured the amount of winter sunshine reaching London in 1970 and found that it had increased by fifty percent! Fog decreased by seventy-five percent. Birds that had not been around for many years returned, including house martins, swifts, and swallows. New insects appeared.

For centuries London had not bothered to remove the thick layers of grime from its famous buildings. When this face-lifting began to be performed in the early 1960's the results were almost too much. Some traditionalists protested that it was a sacrilege to display St. Paul's Cathedral in clean, white stone rather than the familiar sooty black! Others claimed that Sir Christopher Wren, the architect responsible for many London buildings, had intended them to be black. But the outcries soon stopped as Londoners and visitors from all over the world began to enjoy the buildings themselves instead of their camouflage of grime.

London power plants are governed by the Clean Air Act too, and twenty-two of them are constantly monitored by officials to make sure that soot arresters and sulfur-dioxide removers are working. Now, instead of black smoke, plumes of white steam rise from the stacks. In thirty-three boroughs special inspectors continually patrol the streets, watching vigilantly for chimney smoke that is too black. Pollution is measured with a simple card called a Ringelmann Chart, whose shades of gray and black can be compared with chimney smoke that is suspect. If any exceeds Ringelmann Number 2, also known as forty percent obscuration, the inspector knocks on the door and politely visits the offender. Each year there are only a few prosecutions against offenders who refuse to clean up, and practically all the violators lose out in court and are fined.

The Thames, London's famous river, has a notorious pollution history, too. A hundred years ago the Thames had absorbed more sewage, garbage, and industrial waste than it could take and still keep cleaning up the mess. By that time, the purifying bacteria in the water were breaking down sulfates in addition to the nitrates they had worked on for years. Nitrates produce nitrogen gas, which is no particular pollution problem, but sulfates are another story. The gas that results is hydrogen sulfide, generally described as having a "rotten egg" odor, and it began to boil off the Thames and contaminate the city's air. So bad did the stench become that at times Parliament (whose Houses stand along the Thames) was forced to adjourn its sessions.

While the Clean Air Act cleared up the skies, the Port of London Authority got busy on water pollution. In the 1950's the Thames was a running cesspool. Today it is not. By eliminating industrial thermal pollution that had raised the temperature of the river, engineers made it possible for the water to retain more of its oxygen so that bacteria break down less sulfate. Domestic sewage was cleaned up by consolidating 130 small sewage "farms" into half a dozen large, efficient plants. The cleanup of the Thames has cost money, but it has also returned profits. No longer does the Thames stink. Fish from the sea again venture upriver, while freshwater species come down to London as the river becomes livable. Fishermen are taking silver and scarlet roach, and eels are reappearing. The improvement goes on, despite the temporary setback late in 1970 when a strike by sanitation workers again polluted the Thames for a brief period.

In the United States, Pittsburgh has cleaned its smoky skies. True, it still ranks as one of the country's most polluted cities, but it is far better than before the campaign that rid it of much air pollution. Los Angeles is incomparably better than it would have become without diligent smog-abatement efforts. Industrial and domestic burning has been cleaned up or outlawed completely. Automotive pollution remains as the major contributor.

Elsewhere, martyred waterways like Lake Erie, the Potomac River, and others are beginning to get the attention they have needed for years. There are new laws with dedicated enforcers, and a citizenry ready to pay the price for cleaning our air, water, and land. The technology that causes pollution can be made to minimize that pollution. People are beginning to realize that anti-pollution costs in business are as necessary as the costs of manufacturing, distribution, and selling.

Combustion Clean-Up

There are glimmers of hope in the elimination of combustion, too. The "fuel cell," which converts a variety of fuels directly to electricity through chemical processes not involving combustion, has demonstrated its capabilities in vehicles from golf carts to Apollo spacecraft. In Apollo, the fuel cells' "waste product" was pure drinking water. We have a long way to go before fuel cells will provide power in our homes, but a beginning has been made.

It is barely possible that "fusion" power may be a reality by 2000. This scientific and technological accomplishment would rank as more important to mankind than the atom bomb or the computer, for it should make possible unlimited amounts of "clean" power.

A presidential panel reported in 1952 that it would be feasible to heat thirteen million homes in the United States with solar energy by 1975, but so far only a handful of solar houses have been built and operated. Solar water heaters have enjoyed several years of popularity in Japan, Israel, and even in Florida. But some users are switching to "prestige" heat and installing gas or electric heaters, which of course create jobs, profits—and pollution.

In the last several years solar scientist Harold Hay has

The ultimate in pollution-free living is this design for a solar-heated home. Research has also shown that with simple techniques it is possible to cool homes without refrigeration that burns fuel.

—SOLAR ENERGY SOCIETY

designed and built small test houses entirely heated by the sun and kept cool in summer by reflective or insulating panels, and rooftop water ponds; here is pollution-free comfort at practically no cost. The technology for solar space heating is simple and available now. However, inertia, apathy and the availability of fossil fuels argue against this clean and natural way of heating. In fact, our homes are so designed and built that without fuel-fired heating and cooling they are uncomfortable. We are so locked into the conventional fuel system that breaking step will be a major undertaking.

The technology for practical production of power from

solar energy is not yet available, mainly because only token efforts have been made in research and testing. Currently under investigation are a few sophisticated engines for use in orbiting or deep-space craft, most of them converting solar heat into steam or other power. Government research has benefited the "solar battery," which converts sunshine into electric power is a single, simple, and absolutely clean step. A rooftop covered with solar batteries would produce far more electricity than is now consumed in our most modern homes. But few could afford the present price of solar batteries, and without economic incentives the research necessary for lowering these prices will not be done. Obviously the power utilities are not going to fund such studies.

French scientist Georges Claud, who invented the acetylene welding torch, spent great sums of money and years of his time building an STE, or "sea thermal energy" engine. This engine used the difference in heat between water at the surface and that at some depth. Warm water produces steam to drive a turbine, and cold water condenses the steam. The principle is scientifically sound but Claud was unsuccessful in producing a practical engine.

More recently, designers have outlined plans for more efficient STE plants using propane gas instead of water, and built small models to test them. For example, "solar ponds" have been built in Israel to drive low-temperature heat engines. Large installations are envisioned off shore, particularly in tropical waters. These would produce pollution-free electrical power, plus a byproduct in the form of fresh water, a commodity in great demand in much of the world. Such solar-power plants are not presently competitive with coal-fired, or oil-burning facilities. But neither do they pollute the environment or consume limited fuel supplies. It would seem wise to develop these alternative sources of power against the day when pollution becomes unbearable, or we will run out of fuel to cause pollution!

Pollution does not have to be produced in direct proportion to advancing civilization. Instead of equating progress with pollution, we can live in an increasingly cleaner world. A place where we can breathe easily and pleasantly and enjoy the landscape for miles around. Where we can bathe, or boat, or fish in clear, pure water, and eat food that is free of taint. Where rats and disease and filth do not blight neighborhoods and threaten our health and even our lives. We can have this cleaner, better world if we work for it—or we can do nothing and let the world get dirtier and fouler and more deadly. The choice is ours.

SUGGESTED READING

Controlling Pollution, Marshall Goldman, Prentice-Hall, 1967

"An Environment Fit for People," Public Affairs Pamphlet, 1968

"Environmental Quality: The First Annual Report of the Council on Environmental Quality," Government Printing Office, 1970

"Air Pollution Primer," National Tuberculosis and Respiratory Disease Association, 1969

"The Battle for Clean Air," Public Affairs Pamphlet, 1967

With Every Breath You Take, Howard Lewis, Crown, 1965

The Unclean Sky, Louis Battan, Anchor, 1966

The Frail Ocean, Wesley Marx, Coward-McCann, 1967

"A Primer on Waste Water Treatment," Government Printing Office, October 1969

The Water Crisis, D. S. Halacy, Jr., Dutton, 1966

"Waste Management and Control," National Academy of Sciences, 1966

"Report of the Secretary's Commission on Pesticides," Government Printing Office, 1969

Silent Spring, Rachel Carson, Houghton Mifflin, 1962

That We May Live, Jamie Whitten, Van Nostrand, 1966

The Careless Atom, Sheldon Novick, Delta, 1969

"Human Radiobiology," Government Printing Office, 1970

"Nuclear Power and the Environment," Government Printing Office, 1969

"Radiation Exposure Overview: Nuclear Power Reactors and the Population," Dept. of HEW, 1970

A Report on Fallout in Your Food, Roy Hoopes, Signet, 1962

"Noise—Sound Without Value," Government Printing Office, 1968

"Noise, The Third Pollution," Public Affairs Pamphlet, 1970

INDEX